The Ladies of Mischief Interrupt Their Knitting to Present to You,

Needles and Artifice:

A Refined Adventure Story with Ingenious Knitting Patterns

Needles and Artifice
Library of Congress Control Number 2012951029
ISBN 13: 978-1-937513-10-8
First Edition (v1.1)
Published by Cooperative Press
http://www.cooperativepress.com

Every effort has been made to ensure that all the information in this book is accurate at the time of publication, however Cooperative Press neither endorses nor guarantees the content of external links referenced in this book.

If you have questions or comments about this book, or need information about licensing, custom editions, special sales, or academic/corporate purchases, please contact Cooperative Press: info@cooperativepress.com or 13000 Athens Ave C288, Lakewood, OH 44107 USA

For Cooperative Press
Senior Editor: Shannon Okey
Assistant Editor: Elizabeth Green Musselman

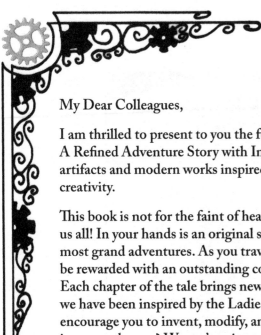

My Dear Colleagues,

I am thrilled to present to you the fully illustrated, annotated, and complete Needles and Artifice: A Refined Adventure Story with Ingenious Knitting Patterns. This is a collection of both historical artifacts and modern works inspired by the Ladies and their spirit of ingenuity, camaraderie, and creativity.

This book is not for the faint of heart; rather, it is a guide to nurture the adventurous potential in us all! In your hands is an original story written by the Ladies of Mischief, recounting one of their most grand adventures. As you travel with them through thrilling quests and exotic locales, you will be rewarded with an outstanding collection of unusual, striking, and engaging knitting patterns. Each chapter of the tale brings new personalities, flavors and perspectives to these designs. Just as we have been inspired by the Ladies and their bold endeavors, so too shall you. And in this spirit we encourage you to invent, modify, and re-imagine these pieces to your heart's content. Where will the journey take you? We can't wait to see.

The project was, of course, the result of an outstanding collaborative effort spanning continents and generations. Our infinite gratitude to all who helped bring this work to fruition: the writers, designers, volunteers, contributors, the Ladies, and now you.

Yours in mischief—today and always,

The Archivist

Contents

Chapter One

In which there are pirates and perils

"I certainly hope our trip to Shanghai is smooth from here. One crash landing was quite enough--"

Anna launched across the table and clapped her hand over Kristoff's mouth, scattering her knitting and her teacup in the process. "Don't!" she hissed, eyes darting from side to side as she scanned the dirigible's galley for danger. Kristoff's strong points included looking fabulous in a suit and making excellent cheese toast, but they did not include Adventuring.

"Don't what?" he attempted to say against her hand, slightly shocked by the unexpected touch. Anna understood his muffled speech, which he found both intriguing and a bit frightening. Anna's eyes returned to his, and she whispered, "Don't tempt fate! You can't say things like that out loud! Try not to even think them, you dolt!" She continued to hold her hand against his mouth for a long moment, listening intently to the sounds of the airship. The boiler bubbled away happily below them, the fire in the stove crackled, and the tea on the table dripped steadily onto the floor. All seemed to be well. She sank back into her chair, and took a bite of her cheese toast. Kristoff found himself missing her touch, and straightened his jacket to cover his discomposure, his thoughts completely distracted from crash landings. Anna chewed her toast, eyes still scanning the room, swallowed, and took a deep breath.

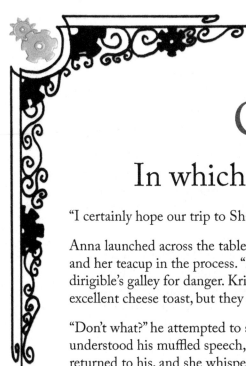

Anna Roisin O'Hare was a feisty inventor with a powerful wanderlust. Born into an Irish family with "new money" and relocated to London as a child, she grew up an outsider and subsequently learned Not To Care What Other People Thought. Growing up with three rowdy siblings gave her a sharp right hook and a willingness to fight dirty. Her letters to the Ladies contained epic tales of adventure (and misadventures) that kept the Ladies in stitches. Anna alternated traveling the world with building unusual and unpredictable mechanical marvels. Her one-woman dirigible, the Arcadia, took her to remote and sometimes surprising destinations. She insisted that she only landed on a house the one time, but the other Ladies never would let her live it down.

"I think we might be--"

KRAK-THOOM! The dirigible shook from a terrible impact, throwing both the travelers to the floor. Anna leaped to her feet in a flash and wasted no time throwing what was left of her cheese toast at her shaken companion.

"You ruddy fool! You had to go and say it!" she shouted at him. The dirigible shook again and Anna flung herself to the galley window. She sucked in a breath between her teeth. "Oh, horse bobbles!"

"What?" Kristoff asked as he staggered over to join her, brushing cheese and crumbs from his coat. "What's happening?"

She spun on her heel and sprinted through the unstable dirigible with ease. "Pirates!" she snarled over her shoulder. "Thrice-frogged pirates!" Another impact, another jarring of the deck beneath their feet. Anna snatched hold of one of the handrails in the hallway and swore again. "And they're shooting

at my ship!" Kristoff struggled into the hallway behind her, brown hair askew and blue eyes worried. "What do we do?" he asked urgently.

"Do?" Anna's smile was manic and a bit terrifying. She leaned over and punched the base of the wall with a sharp movement. A hidden compartment opened, spilling guns and a few long metal knitting needles onto the floor. She chose a rifle and slung it over her shoulder with practiced ease. "We shoot them. We shoot them until they learn not to meddle in our business. Ever again." And with that she darted into the bridge.

Kristoff stood in the hallway for a long moment. Not for the first time, he wondered what he'd gotten himself into. Well, at least it was more interesting than the endless Society balls he would have endured back home. Or worse, his arranged marriage. Fortunately his bride-to-be knew it would be a bad match too, and didn't seem put out at all when he escaped from his engagement party on the back of Anna's horse. He eyed the pile of guns and considered their current predicament. Forming a quick plan, he picked up the rest of the guns and carried the awkward, dangerous pile into the bridge.

Anna spun the wheel freely to the right, bringing the dirigible around and flinging Kristoff into the wall. The pirate's ship was larger, but her ship had maneuverability. She'd seen to that when she built the Arcadia. Kristoff stumbled into the bridge in a clatter of weaponry and she pointed at the controls to her left. "You're on the guns! I need to steer her!" He deposited the weapons in a handy corner and nearly fell onto the controls when the ship shuddered again.

"Anna, perhaps this is a bad time to mention it, but I don't know how to work the guns on your ship!" He clutched at the control panel, heart thumping in his chest. "I didn't even know your ship had guns!" Before Anna could respond, the ship jerked violently to the right, yanking the wheel out of her hands. Anna's heart sank, and she turned to the starboard window to look outside. Her fears were confirmed when she saw that the pirates had a line secured to her ship, and were sliding down from the larger zeppelin above.

"Arse! They're aboard! Forget those guns for the moment! We need to concentrate on these guns!" She snatched up a second rifle and tossed it to Kristoff. He caught it out of the air and quickly checked that it was loaded. Her heart swelled. Her rescued gentleman, all roughed up and ready for action. It made her proud, it really did. Her happy reverie was interrupted by bootsteps on the deck above. "Right. The plan is to shoot them. Remember that."

"I don't entirely know how this sort of... negotiation works." Kristoff squared his shoulders. "I would prefer to avoid bloodshed, if there is a chance of that. I'll wait to shoot until you do. I hate to jump the gun." He managed to look extremely dignified, even as the ship shook around him.

Anna took a deep breath. She hadn't realized all the complications involved in travelling with a real gentleman. She quickly laid out her standard procedure. "We find out what they want. If they want my ship, we're going to shoot them. If they want to rob us, they're going to be terribly disappointed by the lack of cargo. And I will probably shoot them anyway." She paused. "Did you make a pun just there?"

Kristoff tried to ignore her question. "Do things usually end with shooting in these situations?" His voice had a hard note to it even as he tried to smile.

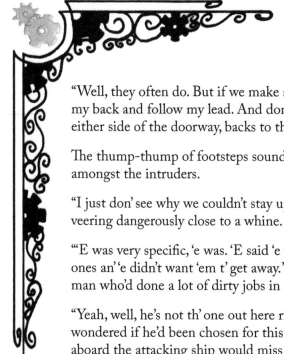

"Well, they often do. But if we make a good entrance, we can probably scare them off. You just watch my back and follow my lead. And don't think I didn't notice that pun." They took up positions on either side of the doorway, backs to the wall. Anna held her finger to her lips and Kristoff nodded.

The thump-thump of footsteps sounded down the hallway. It seemed there was some disagreement amongst the intruders.

"I just don' see why we couldn't stay up in th' ship an' shoot it down." The voice was male and petulant, veering dangerously close to a whine.

"'E was very specific, 'e was. 'E said 'e wanted it done fer sure. 'E said we was after a couple o' slippery ones an' 'e didn't want 'em t' get away." The second voice was older, more cautious. It was a voice of a man who'd done a lot of dirty jobs in his time.

"Yeah, well, he's not th' one out here riskin' his arse, is he?" The petulant voice again. Anna privately wondered if he'd been chosen for this mission because he was terribly annoying and no one back aboard the attacking ship would miss him. Kristoff wondered if he had ever been that annoying in his life. They locked eyes for a moment as the footsteps drew close. Anna nodded, then leaped through the door and smacked the older pirate in the face with her rifle butt. He growled with anger and was about to try to backhand her when he saw Kristoff's rifle pointed at his face from the doorway. He froze. The younger pirate stepped back and lifted a shaky pistol. Anna reversed the rifle and pointed the muzzle into the older pirate's bleeding face.

"You are going to get one chance, and only because I loathe having to deal with messes. Get off my ship." She snarled the last word and the older pirate flinched slightly as a bit of rage spittle flew toward him. The younger pirate looked up and saw Kristoff, and raised an accusing finger to him. "Oi, what're you doing here? You havin' us on?"

Kristoff raised an eyebrow, careful to keep the rifle steady. "I am certain I have no idea what you're talking about." The older pirate smacked the other in the head, hissing, "Ye dunce! Dinnit ye listen? 'E said it was 'is brother!"

Kristoff's other eyebrow raised to join the first. "What? Klaus? Klaus is behind this?" He blinked in shock.

Anna rolled her eyes and waved the end of the rifle barrel around slightly. "Excuse me, but I do still have a gun and I am still entirely willing to use it so if we could hold the conversation for another time I would be entirely grateful now get off my ruddy ship you filthy knots!"

"Right. See, th' thing is…" The older pirate inched backwards, looking somewhat embarrassed. "We're only th' distraction." The younger pirate snapped his head over to look at his partner. "We're th' what?"

The boiler exploded.

Then a lot of things happened very quickly.

Anna screamed obscenities at the top of her lungs, dived for the pirates, and beat them both with her rifle butt. Kristoff's arm around her waist hauled her backwards before she managed more than a couple of good whacks.

The pirates turned tail and ran back to their zeppelin.

Together Anna and Kristoff spun and dove for the dirigible controls as the ship shuddered and began to fall.

There was a sharp twack-thwang sound as the pirate's rope snapped.

The wind screamed past the ship as it lost altitude, helium venting from the envelope.

Anna recovered from her battle rage enough to realize what was happening to the Arcadia, and cried out in mourning. She rose and grabbed Kristoff by the hand, yanking him away from the controls and toward a small hatch in the port side of the bridge. "We can't save her! We have to escape!" A tear streamed down her cheek as she tugged open the hatch and crawled into the padded escape craft on the other side. Kristoff followed with some difficulty.

"It's a bit cramped in here," he commented (with remarkable calm) as he tried to find a place to put his hands that wasn't on Anna. His knees were a lost cause, clearly, so he just left them where they were. Anna managed a small smile while she wriggled around to close the hatch behind them, accidentally kicking him in the stomach in the process.

"Well, it's only meant for one. Two is pushing it. And I brought the rifle." There! The hatch was shut! She wriggled around again until she was face-to-face with Kristoff, then reached up for the release lever. "Hold on to something."

"There's nothing to hold on to!" he protested, managing to blush a little bit despite the life-threatening danger.

Anna shrugged. "Have it your way, then."

She yanked the lever.

The pod erupted from its housing, and fell for what seemed like forever.

With a FOOMP and an abrupt jerk, the parachute deployed and the pod began to drift calmly and sedately toward the rocky ground. A gentle thump and a short roll later and it came to a stop.

Anna took a deep breath and released her death-grip on Kristoff's shoulders. She reached up and popped the exit hatch on the top of the escape pod, hoping that they weren't surrounded by bears. Again. The scent of jasmine floated into the tiny pod, completely untainted by the smell of bears, Anna noted with satisfaction. She tried to sit up but found herself impeded by Kristoff's grip on her waist, his head buried in her shoulder and his eyes squeezed shut. A smile played across her mouth as she relaxed back into the protective padding of the escape craft. Was it wrong to enjoy this moment? Hmm... Anna decided that even if it was wrong, she didn't care very much.

Kristoff opened his eyes a moment later. He was alive? He was alive! They'd landed! He was (reasonably) safe! And he was hugging Anna! He was hugging Anna?! He was out of the escape craft like a shot, panting from nerves, embarrassment and... something else. "Sorry! I'm so sorry! There wasn't anything else to hold on to, I didn't mean to presume!"

Anna popped her head out of the hatch and raised a thoroughly exasperated eyebrow at him. "I'm sorry, was I complaining? Because I was fairly certain I wasn't complaining. If that's how this is going to go, though, then fine." She stood up, slung her rifle back over her shoulder and yanked the mandatory bag of emergency supplies out of the escape craft. She threw it to Kristoff with perhaps a bit more force than necessary and after struggling through the remains of the jasmine bush they'd landed in she stalked off down the hill to the smoking remains of the Arcadia. After a moment, Kristoff followed, having a gentlemanly argument with himself in his head.

Oh, poor Arcadia. It was the end. There was just no way to salvage her. The crash had been violent, sending bits of the ship all over the wide meadow. Anna dropped to her knees next to a large pile and reached out a hand to touch a shattered teapot, the knitted cozy still intact. Her face crumpled and her shoulders shook with silent sobs.

****

Far away in foggy London, two shaking but still graceful hands fiddled with the dials and knobs on a large mechanical box. The box's giant antenna shifted and spun to tune to a particular aether frequency. It was time for Johanna Obscura to begin her midday check in on the Ladies. She turned the right knob a few degrees further, and was rewarded with a small chime as her machine located the first lady. She lay back in her bed to rest her hands and took a moment to enjoy the genius of her machine. Ever since her nearly fatal lab accident, she barely had the strength to lift a wrench. While at first she was deeply frustrated, she soon discovered that her dear Ladies and their clever Mechanists were capable of assembling the masterwork creation she dreamed of. When it first ran she cried with joy. Not only did it keep her connected to her friends as they traveled the world, it also worked so smoothly and effortlessly that she could operate it even on her worst days.

Miss Johanna Obscura was the photography expert for the Ladies. Her fascination with Photography and Technology drove her to perform increasingly unusual experiments. Her greatest triumph and greatest tragedy occurred on the same fateful day. She had captured the world's first aether-transmitted photographic image, the largest breakthrough in both Photography and Aetheric Studies of her time. However, Science is a harsh mistress, and even in victory she does not let the scientist rest. Miss Obscura pushed her machinery to its limits. Disaster struck when a tiny gear inside the machine snapped, causing a massive explosion of gears, steam, and glass plate fragments. Miss Johanna Obscura was sliced, crushed, and burned by her machine, and nearly died. Miss Obscura's only solace during her painful recovery came during her visits from her dear friends, the fellow members of The Ladies of Mischief. The ladies' tales of adventures around the world kept her imagination fired and her healing sides shaking with painful, glorious laughter. She began to dream of a way to capture images of these adventures, and her new course of scientific discovery began. Confined to bed, she developed clever aetheric cameras hidden in brooches, thus maintaining her connection to the Ladies during their world travels.

The machine chimed again, indicating that the first image was complete. She reset the dials and knobs to a new frequency, narrowing in on the next lady. After a moment of rest, she pressed the button that would raise the latest image up so she could view it.

Her eyebrows came together as the image lifted into view. Anna's dirigible was completely destroyed! This was far beyond just a crash landing. Anyone could see that repairs were out of the question. From the angle of the image she deduced that Anna was kneeling next to the wreckage, definitely grieving, possibly injured. She immediately rang for a servant to bring her the previous night's image from Anna and her star charts. Her hands steadied and her pain fell away as she began to activate her trickiest and most ingenious invention yet...

****

Kristoff limped up to Anna's kneeling form, hesitated a moment, then placed his hand gently on her shoulder.

"My ship... My Arcadia. Oh, my poor ship." Kristoff pretended gallantly not to see as she scrubbed tears from her eyes. "She's been with me so long. I built her..." Anna's hands began to shake with anger. She leapt up and grabbed Kristoff by the collar, their faces inches apart.

"Back on the ship. Those felted pirates! They said your brother was behind this." Anna's eyes were hard little diamonds of hate. Her lip curled. "I am going to find him. And I am going to make him pay for what he did to my ship." She released his collar and he took an involuntary step backwards. For a split second, he almost pitied Klaus. Almost.

Kristoff cleared his throat. "Um. Anna? I must point out that apparently my brother wants both of us dead. I don't think he was after your ship..." He trailed off as her diamond gaze turned back on him. He held his hands up to ward her off. "No. You're quite right. The destruction of the noble Arcadia is much more important than our lives."

With one last angry glare, Anna turned to the rubble, and began shifting through it with a practiced hand. Kristoff joined her after a moment, and they managed to retrieve a portion of Anna's weapon collection and (ridiculously, Kristoff thought) a rather large bag of Ceylon tea before either spoke again.

"How exactly are we going to get out of here, Anna?"

Anna shrugged and made a vague gesture. "We can figure that out later. Aha!" She held aloft a waterproof leather knitting bag. "My siblings laughed when I made this bag, but look what survived a dirigible explosion and crash!"

Kristoff would not be distracted. "Figure it out later? We're wrecked in the middle of nowhere and –"

DINGdingWHIRRRdingDINGDINGwhirrrDING! The brooch on Anna's hat lit up and pulsed with a manic code. Kristoff stared at it, agog. She'd never taken the hat off and he'd rather wondered why, but he'd certainly never expected it to do that. Anna, for her part, simply cocked her head and listened carefully. After a long moment, the brooch quieted and returned to normal. Anna nodded calmly and smiled at Kristoff.

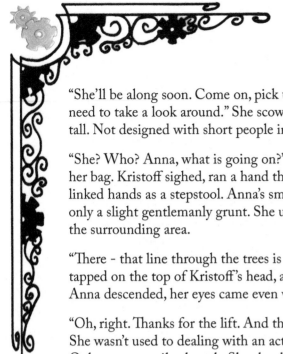

"She'll be along soon. Come on, pick up what you can, we're leaving. Wait, first give me a boost - I need to take a look around." She scowled at a nearby stand of bamboo. "All this nature is too ruddy tall. Not designed with short people in mind, I'll tell you that."

"She? Who? Anna, what is going on?" The only response was a smirk as Anna pulled a spyglass from her bag. Kristoff sighed, ran a hand through his increasingly disheveled hair, then bent to offer his linked hands as a stepstool. Anna's small boot fit easily in his hands, and he managed to lift her with only a slight gentlemanly grunt. She used the top of his head to stabilize, and the spyglass to peer at the surrounding area.

"There - that line through the trees is far too straight to be natural. That's where we're headed." She tapped on the top of Kristoff's head, and he gently lowered her to the ground with an inward sigh. As Anna descended, her eyes came even with his. An unusual sinking feeling started in her chest.

"Oh, right. Thanks for the lift. And the help with salvage. I'm also quite glad you survived the crash." She wasn't used to dealing with an actual gentlemen. His quiet dignity momentarily unnerved her. Only momentarily, though. She shook her head and picked up her knitting satchel.

"Grab what you can and let's go." Hands full, she spared one last long look for the remains of the Arcadia. Her sadness turned into a solid lump of anger. She turned and stomped into the woods, with Kristoff following at a polite distance.

Kristoff was relieved when their destination turned out to be a train track. He sorely hoped that the next passing train would be populated with civilized folk who might have some tea to share. Or just hot water, as they had plenty of tea with them. Anna plopped down on the ground and begin digging in her bag. "Mmm... yes, I think the red wool will be best." She pulled a stocking with bright red stripes from the bag and began knitting on it. Kristoff sighed, picked a relatively clean spot of ground, and settled down to wait.

It was some time later when the sound of a train echoed through the air, and Anna stood up and began waving the stocking over her head. "Kristoff," she said rather smugly as the steam train came into view and slowed to a halt. "I'd like you to meet one of my fellow Ladies of Mischief, Miss Caldonia Kitty Dexterhaven. We usually just call her Kitty. She's our ride."

****

Miss Caldonia Kitty Dexterhaven had been sorting her latest botanical samples when her brooch began an alarming racket. The dings and whirs of the brooch were almost in time with the rocking of the train car, creating a strange kind of mechanical harmony. It took her several moments to transition her mind from Latin

Caldonia Kitty Dexterhaven was an intrepid botanist and the Ladies' connection to the vast railway system of Dexterhaven Locomotives. She was particularly interested in collecting both botanical samples from around the world, and men. She found it most convenient and pleasing to have a variety of men as her personal servants as she traveled the world. Her botanical collection threatened to overtake the entire main house of the Dexterhaven Estate, but her thirst for knowledge and adventure never stopped. She was always on the first train out on every new rail line, eager to see new vistas and gather ever more samples of fascinating foreign flora.

to the special code developed by the Ladies. She straightened up in her seat as she realized that the broadcast was directed to her.

"Ashby dear, leave off that and bring me my memorandum book." Her personal secretary reluctantly stopped massaging her stocking clad foot and released it with a sigh. "And don't be so petulant. Come on, this message is important!"

Mr. Ashby Delmar stood, bowed, and quickly retrieved her ornately decorated memorandum book from a secret desk compartment. As he handed it to her, Caldonia rewarded him with a warm smile and a slight lowering of her eyelids. But pleasure must wait when a fellow Lady has gotten herself into danger. With a slight frown, she transcribed the message, checked the coordinates on the third repetition, and by the fourth repetition she was striding through the train compartments to speak with her conductor.

It was most fortunate that Caldonia was aboard the Dexterhaven Orient Line when the calamity occurred. The new rail line from Constantinople to Shanghai had presented an irresistible opportunity to gather botanical samples from eastern China, an area in which her collection was sorely lacking.

Her truly impressive "field kit" fit snugly inside the largest locomotive car that Dexterhaven Locomotives manufactured. Her personal train car, a traveling bedroom, salon, and study, was part of the first train to travel the Orient Line. Her gentlemen in waiting occupied another two cars attached to hers, with her field kit at the end of the line. After the Northeastern Dinosaur Fern Spore Bloom Incident, her father had insisted that her specimens be kept as far as possible from the train passengers. The remote location meant that Caldonia was a touch winded by the time she had made her way to the conductor.

"Mr. Beringsley –" she panted, "–I must know our current location –" Another pant. "–Immediately!"

"We crossed the Yangtsze about two hours ago, so we're about four hours out from Shanghai, Miss." He fumbled with a book containing information about the new rail line. "Looks like we're in Jiangsu Province, Rail Track section #543". He snapped the book shut.

"Excellent! Stop the train immediately, Mr. Beringsley." Caldonia turned from the window and gave the conductor a look that quelled his protest before he could do more than open his mouth. He reached for the brake.

The train shuddered as the brakes were applied, and the massive bulk slowed. Caldonia watched out the forward windows as the train continued to move through the Chinese countryside. She straightened up and proclaimed "The train must stop now, Mr. Beringsley." She held on as the conductor applied the full brake and the train lurched slightly.

"Thank you Mr. Beringsley. Mr. Delmar, please prepare a compartment for a dear friend of mine. It looks like she has a companion as well- and I'm sure they are in dire need of some tea."

As Caldonia stepped off her train, her footsteps slowed in confusion. Anna was covered in ashes and wearing the marks of recent tears on her face, yet was smiling quite smugly. A somewhat awkward gentleman stood beside her, holding a bizarre assortment of items but still maintaining an air of dignity.

"It is lovely to see a friend, even in dire circumstances. Come aboard, and bring that fabulous stocking with you. We will be arriving in Shanghai in about four hours, and I have a desperate desire to hear your tale over some knitting and tea."

The Resilience Top

By: Sarra Loew

DESCRIPTION:
Ribbed short-sleeved tunic with very open stitch pattern. Knit bottom up in one piece to armholes. Slip stitch edging on front bands. Shaping is accomplished through negative ease and by changing needle sizes. Two inch beaded edge along bottom.

SPECIAL TECHNIQUES:
Brioche Rib: yo, sl1, k2tog

Add Bead: Load bead onto crochet hook. Slip the last stitch worked (a k2tog) off the needle and hook it with the crochet hook. Slide the bead off the crochet hook and onto the stitch. Put the stitch back onto the right needle.

In yarn, industry, and Ladies alike, resilience is the quality of 'bouncing back' after stress and strain. This fitted brioche stitch top exudes an air of sweetness, over a foundation of steel. Brilliantly stretching and shifting to fit your every curve - you'll be ready to face whatever the day brings in style.

FINISHED DIMENSIONS:
Bust: 24 (28, 30, 35, 38, 42)"
Waist: 19 (22, 24, 28, 31, 34)"
Hips: 27 (31, 34, 39, 43, 47)"
Length: 19¼ (19¾, 20¼, 21, 21¼, 22)"

NOTE: The fabric will stretch 1-2" lengthwise. Some length has been removed to account for this tendency, so the finished dimensions should be a bit short on you.

TO FIT BODY MEASUREMENTS:
Bust: 28 (32, 36, 40, 44, 48)"
Waist: 20 (24, 28, 32, 36, 40)"
Hips: 28 (32, 36, 40, 44, 48)"

The Brioche Rib is very stretchy, which has been utilized in the sizing. If you are between sizes, refer to the list below of the maximum dimensions each size will support while maintaining a pleasing fabric.

Maximum dimensions:
Bust: 30 (34, 38, 43, 48, 52)"
Waist: 30 (34, 38, 43, 48, 52)"
Hips: 38 (43, 47, 54, 60, 65)"

EASE:
4-6" negative ease

YARN AND YARDAGE:
Nautilace by Cephalopod Yarns, http://cephalopodyarns.com
60% silk, 40% baby camel; 400yds (366m) per 57g; lace weight
Color: Blue Spot Angelfish, 2 (2, 3, 3, 4, 4) skeins

Yarn special features for substitution: choose a heavy laceweight/light fingering yarn. A silk blend will add shine and smoothness.

GAUGE:
Ball band gauge of chosen yarn: 24-32 sts = 4"
Knitted and blocked gauge:
In stockinette (stockinette swatch should be washed and firmly blocked to even up stitches):
Large needle (US 9): 23 sts x 21 rows = 4"/10cm
Small needle (US 6): 24 sts x 33 rows = 4"/10cm

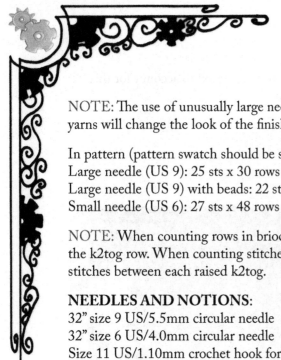

NOTE: The use of unusually large needles for the yarn weight leads to an open, lacy look. Heavier yarns will change the look of the finished piece.

In pattern (pattern swatch should be steam blocked only - never wet blocked):
Large needle (US 9): 25 sts x 30 rows = 4"/10cm
Large needle (US 9) with beads: 22 sts x 28 rows = 4"/10cm
Small needle (US 6): 27 sts x 48 rows = 4"/10cm

NOTE: When counting rows in brioche stitch, each k2tog represents two rows - the slipped row and the k2tog row. When counting stitches in brioche stitch, count the raised k2tog as 1 stitch, with two stitches between each raised k2tog.

NEEDLES AND NOTIONS:
32" size 9 US/5.5mm circular needle
32" size 6 US/4.0mm circular needle
Size 11 US/1.10mm crochet hook for beads
Size 5/F US/3.74mm crochet hook to pick up dropped stitches (strongly advised!)
18 (19, 19, 20, 20, 20) buttons
400 (450, 500, 575, 650, 725) size 6/0 seed beads

PATTERN NOTES:
The Brioche Rib fabric is very stretchy, and the suggested yarn is very slippery. The fabric responds really well to stretching, either vertically or horizontally. Feel free to pull on the fabric as you knit it to distribute the yarn and even out your stitches. The slipped stitch edging looks best after a good tug. Start with your swatch, and notice how much the fabric changes when pulled lengthwise vs. widthwise. The weight of the beads will pull the fabric lengthwise, helping it to conform to the body.

Fixing mistakes:
The Brioche Rib is simple to execute, but can be tricky to fix when you make a mistake. Before you begin the garment, you must knit a swatch in order to get accustomed to the stitch pattern. Deliberately drop a stitch and use the instructions below to learn how to fix this common mistake. Once you have learned how to correct a dropped stitch in your swatch, you're ready to start the garment. The pattern does not appear until about 8 rows are completed.

To fix a dropped stitch:
Use your crochet hook to capture the dropped stitch. Each stitch is actually a k2tog, combining the stitch slipped on the previous row and the yarn over. You will be picking up the next stitch through two strands of yarn. Use your crochet hook to reach under the yarn over strand (which is connected to the two purl stitches on either side of the current stitch), and hook the other strand. Pull the strand through the existing loop on the crochet hook to pick up one stitch. Look closely at the surrounding stitches to see if the yarn strands are creating the same fabric. If they don't look the same, drop the stitch you just created and try again. It often takes a few tries to learn how to correct this mistake, but with a bit of practice you can master it.

Pattern

Body:

Cast on 196 (224, 252, 284, 312, 344) stitches using any very stretchy cast on.

Setup Row (ws): k6, pm, *yo, sl1, k3tog,* repeat between * to the last six stitches, pm, k2, sl4 pwise wyif.

NOTE: The slipped stitch edge will roll like an i-cord. The first stitch tends to be pretty loose when knit, but snugs up nicely as you go.

Work the following pattern rows 1-2 until you have a total of 16 pattern rows, including two buttonhole rows.

Work Buttonhole Row on Row 5, then every ten rows afterwards (should be on a rs row). After the first 16 rows, omit the beads when working the buttonhole row. Total buttonholes: 18 (19, 19, 20, 20, 20)

Pattern Row 1 (rs): k6, sm, *yo, sl1, k2tog, ab,* repeat between * to the last 6 stitches, sm, k2, sl4 pwise wyif.

Pattern Row 2 (ws): k6, sm, *yo, sl1, k2tog,* repeat between * to the last six stitches, sm, k2, sl4 pwise wyif.

Buttonhole Row (rs): k4, yo, k2tog, sm, *yo, sl1, k2tog, ab,* repeat between * to the last six stitches, sm, k2, sl4 pwise wyif.

NOTE: When counting rows, the raised k2tog stitch represents two rows - it was slipped in the first row, and k2tog in the second row.

Work the following pattern rows 1-2 until you have 28 pattern rows (3"), including the beaded section.

Pattern Row 1 (rs): k6, sm, *yo, sl1, k2tog,* repeat between * to the last six stitches, sm, k2, sl4 pwise wyif.

Pattern Row 2 (ws): k6, sm, *yo, sl1, k2tog,* repeat between * to the last six stitches, sm, k2, sl4 pwise wyif.

Waist Section:
Switch to small needle and continue to work rows 1-2 until you have a total of 106 (106, 109, 109, 109, 112) rows, or piece measures 9½ (9½, 9¾, 9¾, 9¾, 10) inches.

Bust Section:
Change to large needle and work rows 1-2 for another 30 rows or 4 inches. Begin working fronts and back separately, starting with the right front.

Right Front:
rs: work 39 (45, 51, 57, 63, 69) stitches in pattern as established, then turn work.
ws: BO 3 (6, 6, 9, 9, 9) sts purlwise, purling the yo through the back loop.

K2 (passing the final BO stitch over the first k stitch), then k the yo through the back loop, to establish the armhole edging (3 knit/slipped stitches). Work the remaining stitches in pattern as established, including edging stitches.

Total right front stitches: 36 (39, 45, 48, 54, 60)

Size 28, 32: skip to the All Sizes section below.
Size 36, 40, 44, 48:
Decrease as follows:
Row 1 (rs): work in pattern to the last 6 stitches (one brioche set and three edge stitches), p1, k2tog, slip the last 3 stitches pwise wyif.
Row 2 (ws): k3, p2tog, work in pattern to end.
Row 3 (rs): work in pattern to last 4 stitches, k1, slip the last 3 stitches pwise wyif.
Row 4 (ws): k2, k2tog, work in pattern to end.

Total right front stitches: 42 (45, 51, 57)

Decrease one stitch every other row as follows:
Row 1 (rs): work in pattern to the last 6 stitches, p1, k2tog, slip the last 3 stitches pwise wyif.
Row 2 (ws): k3, p1, k1, work in pattern to end.
Row 3 (rs): work to last five stitches, k2tog, slip the last 3 stitches pwise wyif.
Row 4 (ws): k3, p1, work in pattern to end.

Row 5 (rs): work to last 7 stitches, p1, k2tog, k1, slip the last 3 stitches pwise wyif.
Row 6 (ws): k3, p2, k1, work in pattern to end.
Row 7 (rs): work to last 6 stitches, p1, k2tog, slip the last 3 stitches pwise wyif.
Row 8 (ws): k3, p1, k1, work in pattern to end.
Row 9 (rs): work to last 5 stitches, k2tog, slip the last 3 stitches pwise wyif.
Row 10 (ws): k3, p1, work in pattern to end.
Row 11 (rs): work to last 4 stitches, k1, slip the last 3 stitches pwise wyif.
Row 12 (ws): k2, k2tog, work in pattern to end.
Total right front stitches: 39 (42, 48, 54)

Size 48 only:
Repeat rows 1-12 once more. Total right front stitches: 48

All Sizes:
Work in established pattern, with slipped stitch edging on both edges and maintaining buttonholes, for 37 (41, 27, 32, 34, 26) more rows, or until front measures 5 (5½, 5¾, 6½, 6¾, 7½) inches from armhole bindoff without stretching. End on a ws row.

Neck Bindoff:
Row 1 (rs): BO 6 (6, 6, 6, 9, 9) stitches at the front neck edge, removing marker. After working the last BO stitch, hold the yarn to the back, slip the next stitch to the right needle, and pass the BO stitch over it. Slip the stitch back to the left needle and start the brioche pattern as usual, with a yo. Work in pattern to last three stitches, and slip the last 3 stitches pwise wyif.
Row 2 (ws): k3, work in Brioche Rib pattern to end.
Row 3 (rs): BO 9 (9, 9, 9, 12, 12) stitches, work in pattern to last 3 stitches, slip the last 3 stitches pwise wyif.
Row 4 (ws): k3, work in Brioche Rib pattern to end.
Row 5 (rs): work in pattern to last three stitches, slip the last 3 stitches pwise wyif.
Row 6 (ws): k3, work in pattern to end.

Bind off loosely, continuing to k2tog the yo and slipped stitch. This means you will be binding off two stitches for each three stitch brioche set at the shoulders. Break yarn.

Back:
Join yarn and begin working the next set of live stitches.
rs: BO 3 (6, 6, 9, 9, 9) stitches knitwise, knitting the yo through the back loop.
K2 (passing the final BO stitch over the first k stitch), then k the yo through the back loop, to establish the armhole edging (3 knit/slipped stitches). Work in established pattern for 66 (72, 81, 90, 99, 111) stitches, turn work.

ws: BO 3 (6, 6, 9, 9, 9) stitches purlwise, purling the yo through the back loop.
K2 (passing the final BO stitch over the first k stitch), then k the yo through the back loop, to begin the armhole edging (3 knit/slipped stitches). Work in established pattern to last three stitches, slip the last 3 stitches pwise wyif.

Total back stitches: 66 (69, 78, 84, 93, 105)

Size 28, 32: skip to the All Sizes section below.

Size 36, 40, 44, 48:
Decrease as follows:
Row 1 (rs): k3, p1, k2tog, work to last 6 stitches, p1, k2tog, slip the last 3 stitches pwise wyif.
Row 2 (ws): k3, p2tog, work in pattern to last 5 stitches, p2tog, slip the last 3 stitches pwise wyif.
Row 3 (rs): k2, k2tog, work to last 4 stitches, k1, slip the last 3 stitches pwise wyif.
Row 4 (ws): k2, k2tog, work to last 3 stitches, slip the last 3 stitches pwise wyif.

Total back stitches: 72 (78, 87, 99)

Decrease two stitches every other row as follows:
Row 1 (rs): k3, p1, k2tog, work in pattern to last 6 stitches, p1, k2tog, slip the last 3 sts pwise wyif.
Row 2 (ws): k3, p1, k1, work in pattern to last 5 stitches, p1, k1, slip the last 3 stitches pwise wyif.
Row 3 (rs): k3, k2tog, work in pattern to last five stitches, k2tog, slip the last 3 stitches pwise wyif.
Row 4 (ws): k3, p1, work in pattern to last 4 stitches, p1, slip the last 3 stitches pwise wyif.
Row 5 (rs): k4, p1, k2tog, work to last 7 stitches, p1, k2tog, k1, slip the last 3 stitches pwise wyif.
Row 6 (ws): k3, p2, k1, work in pattern to last 6 stitches, p1, k1, p1, slip the last 3 stitches pwise wyif.
Row 7 (rs): k4, k2tog, work to last 6 stitches, p1, k2tog, slip the last 3 stitches pwise wyif.
Row 8 (ws): k3, p1, k1, work in pattern to last 5 stitches, p2, slip the last 3 stitches pwise wyif.
Row 9 (rs): k3, k2tog, work to last 5 stitches, k2tog, slip the last 3 stitches pwise wyif.
Row 10 (ws): k3, p1, work in pattern to last 4 stitches, p1, slip the last 3 stitches pwise wyif.
Row 11 (rs): k2, k2tog, work to last 4 stitches, k1, slip the last 3 stitches pwise wyif.
Row 12 (ws): k2, k2tog, work in pattern to last 3 stitches, slip the last 3 stitches pwise wyif.

Total back stitches: 60 (66, 75, 87)

Size 48 only:
Repeat rows 1-12 once more.
Total back stitches: 75

All Sizes:
Work in established pattern, with slipped stitch edging on both edges, for 37 (41, 27, 32, 34, 26) more rows, or until back measures 5 (5½, 5¾, 6½, 6¾, 7½) inches from armhole bindoff without stretching.

Bind off loosely, continuing to k2tog the yo and slipped stitch. This means you will be binding off two stitches for each three stitch brioche set at the shoulders. Break yarn.

Left Front:
Join yarn and begin working the final set of live stitches.
rs: BO 3 (6, 6, 9, 9, 9) stitches purlwise, purling the yo through the back loop.
K2 (passing the final BO stitch over the first k stitch), then k the yo through the back loop, to establish the armhole edging (3 knit/slipped stitches). Work the remaining stitches in pattern as established, including edging stitches.
ws: work in established pattern to last three stitches, slip the last 3 stitches pwise wyif.

Total left front stitches: 36 (39, 45, 48, 54, 60)

Size 28, 32: skip to the All Sizes section below.
Size 36, 40, 44, 48:
Decrease as follows:
Row 1 (rs): k3, p1, k2tog, work to end.
Row 2 (ws): work to last 5 stitches, p2tog, slip the last 3 stitches pwise wyif.
Row 3 (rs): k2, k2tog, work to end.
Row 4 (ws): work to last 3 stitches, slip the last 3 stitches pwise wyif.

Total left front stitches: 42 (45, 51, 57)

Decrease one stitch every other row as follows:
Row 1 (rs): k3, p1, k2tog, work in pattern to end.
Row 2 (ws): work to last 5 stitches, p1, k1, slip the last 3 stitches pwise wyif.
Row 3 (rs): k3, k2tog, work in pattern to end.
Row 4 (ws): work to last 4 stitches, p1, slip the last 3 stitches pwise wyif.
Row 5 (rs): k4, p1, k2tog, work to end.
Row 6 (ws): work to last 6 stitches, p1, k1, p1, slip the last 3 stitches pwise wyif.
Row 7 (rs): k4, k2tog, work to end.
Row 8 (ws): work to last 5 stitches, p2, slip the last 3 stitches pwise wyif.
Row 9 (rs): k3, k2tog, work to end.
Row 10 (ws): work to last 4 stitches, p1, slip the last 3 stitches pwise wyif.
Row 11 (rs): k2, k2tog, work to end.
Row 12 (ws): k3, work to end.

Total left front stitches: 39 (42, 48, 54)

Size 48 only:
Repeat rows 1-12 once more. Total left front stitches: 48

All Sizes:
Work in established pattern, with slipped stitch edging on both edges and maintaining buttonholes, for 37 (41, 27, 32, 34, 26) more rows, or until front measures 5¾ (6¼, 6¾, 7½, 7¾, 8¼) inches from armhole bindoff without stretching.

Neck Bindoff:
Row 1 (ws): bind off 6 (6, 6, 6, 9, 9) stitches at the front neck edge. For the last BO stitch, hold the yarn to the back, slip the next stitch to the right needle, and pass the BO stitch over it. Then slip the stitch back to the left needle and start the brioche pattern as usual, with a yo. Work in pattern to last three stitches, slip the last 3 stitches pwise wyif.
Row 2 (rs): k3, work in Brioche Rib pattern to end.
Row 3 (ws): bind off 9 (9, 9, 9, 12, 12) stitches, work in pattern to last 3 stitches, slip the last 3 stitches pwise wyif.
Row 4 (rs): k3, work in Brioche Rib pattern to end.
Row 5 (ws): work in pattern to last three stitches, slip the last 3 stitches pwise wyif.
Row 6 (rs): k3, work in pattern to end.

Bind off loosely, continuing to k2tog the yo and slipped stitch. This means you will be binding off two stitches for each three stitch brioche set at the shoulders. Break yarn.

BODY FINISHING:
Reinforce the buttonholes by overcast stitching around them. The slip stitch edge provides a convenient location to hide the yarn ends.

Lay the tunic out flat. Gently tug the fabric lengthwise and widthwise alternating, to even out the stitches. End with a lengthwise pull. Make sure that the beads are sitting correctly, as they can migrate a bit while you're working on the tunic. Once you steam block the piece with the beads correctly arranged, they will stay in place.

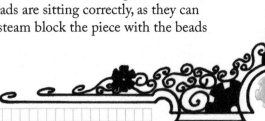

Once the beads are arranged correctly, steam block the tunic, pulling the slipped stitch edge to tighten it. Make sure to keep the brioche rib gathered and fluffy - don't flatten it out. Let it dry completely. Sew the shoulders together with the back.

Sleeves:

Left Sleeve:

Using larger needle, pick up 20 (22, 22, 24, 24, 24) stitches through the interior edge stitch (the first stitch knit, which lays inside the edge - the other two stitches of the edging should still appear on the front) along the left front armhole edge, starting 3 (3, 5, 6, 8, 12) rows above the armhole bindoff row, and ending at the shoulder. Picking up in the edge stitch means that you will be picking up one stitch for every two rows.

Begin working at the shoulder seam.

Setup Row (ws): *yo, sl1, k1,* repeat between * to last 2 stitches, slip pwise wyif.
Row 1 (rs): k2,*yo, sl1, k2tog,* repeat between * to end.
Row 2 (ws): *yo, sl1, k2tog,* repeat between * to last 2 stitches, slip pwise wyif.

Repeat Rows 1-2 until you have a total of 53 (54, 56, 60, 62, 64) rows, or 7 (7¼, 7½, 8, 8¼, 8½) inches in length.

Bind off loosely, continuing to k2tog the yo and slipped stitch. This means you will be binding off two stitches for each three stitch brioche set. Sew the BO edge to the interior edge stitch on the back armhole, so that the two other edge stitches still appear on the exterior. Thread a strand of yarn through every second stitch along the top edge of the sleeve, and use it to gather the sleeve edge tightly, then tie the yarn. Sew the top edge of the sleeve to the interior of the shoulder to create a puff sleeve.

Right Sleeve:

Pick up the stitches along the right front armhole as above. Begin working at the shoulder seam.

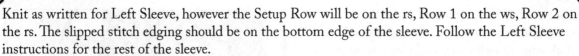

Knit as written for Left Sleeve, however the Setup Row will be on the rs, Row 1 on the ws, Row 2 on the rs. The slipped stitch edging should be on the bottom edge of the sleeve. Follow the Left Sleeve instructions for the rest of the sleeve.

Neck:
Pick up 15 (15, 15, 15, 21, 21) stitches along the right front top, 30 (27, 27, 30, 39, 39) stitches along the back and 15 (15, 15, 15, 21, 21) stitches along left front top.

Setup row (ws): k2, *yo, sl1, k1,* repeat between * to last 2 stitches, slip pwise wyif.

Row 1 (rs): k2, *yo, sl1, k2tog,* repeat between * to last 2 stitches, slip pwise wyif.
Row 2 (ws): k2, *yo, sl1, k2tog,* repeat between * to last 2 stitches, slip pwise wyif.

Repeat Rows 1-2 until you have a total of 10 rows. Bind off loosely, continuing to k2tog the yo and slipped stitch. This means you will be binding off two stitches for each three stitch brioche set. Sew the BO edge to the interior of the neck, making sure to line up the ribs.

Sew on buttons. Enjoy!

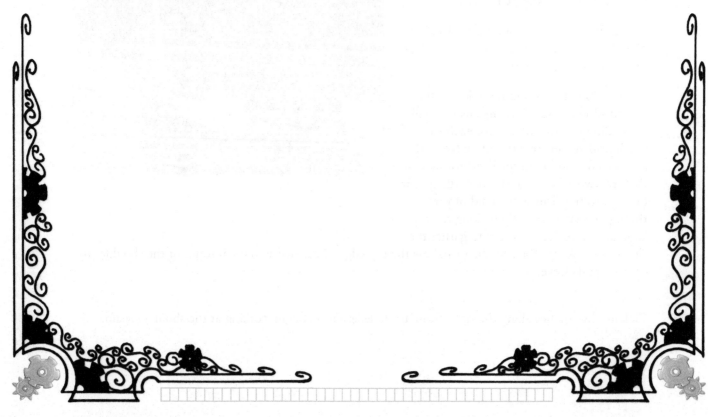

The Rivet Spats
By: Katrina Elsaesser

DESCRIPTION:
Knee-high spats with side button closures. Clever shaping and visual interest are created by a bias motif front panel and Half-Twisted Rib back panel.

FINISHED DIMENSIONS:
Front Panel (total length of leg and foot): 5¼" wide x 17" tall

Back Panel: 5¼" wide (plus stretch) x 15" tall

TO FIT BODY MEASUREMENTS:
Leg circumference: 10-16"
Additional stitches can be easily added to accommodate other sizes.

Railway travel can be murder on your stockings! Leave it to the Ladies to merge function with fancy. Equal parts daring and darling, these spats provide both warmth and protection from flying sparks and pointy bits. A quick, bulky knit, infinitely customizable for color, height, buttons and bows. Who's got the prettiest armor?

YARN AND YARDAGE:
Bulky by Actual Size Creations,
http://valutree.etsy.com
100% superwash merino; 125yds (114m) per 114g; bulky weight
Color: Jasper, 2 skeins

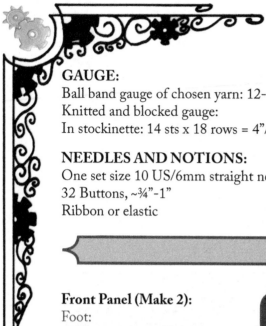

GAUGE:
Ball band gauge of chosen yarn: 12-15 sts = 4"
Knitted and blocked gauge:
In stockinette: 14 sts x 18 rows = 4"/10cm

NEEDLES AND NOTIONS:
One set size 10 US/6mm straight needles
32 Buttons, ~¾"-1"
Ribbon or elastic

Pattern

Front Panel (Make 2):
Foot:
CO 9 stitches.

Row 1 (ws): purl all stitches.
Row 2 (rs): k2, m1l, knit to 2 stitches from the end, m1r, k2. (11 sts)
Row 3 (ws): purl.

Repeat Rows 2 and 3 until you have 21 sts, ending with a purl row.

NOTE: Add additional repeats here for a wider/longer foot.

If tying with ribbon, work the following two rows:

Row 4 (rs): k2, yo2, k2tog, k13, ssk, yo2, k2.
Row 5 (ws): p3, k1, ssp, p11, p2tog, p, k, p2.

If securing with elastic, work 1 knit row and 1 purl row instead.

Ankle:
Row 1 (rs): k2, k2tog, k6, m1l, k1, m1r, k6, ssk, k2 (21 sts).
Row 2 (ws): purl.
Repeat these two rows four more times.

NOTE: To widen the ankle/leg at any point, simply eliminate the k2tog/ssk from any right side row as follows: k10, m1l, k1, m1r, k10. 2 sts increased.

Leg:
Row 1 (rs): k2, yo, k2tog, k6, m1l, k1, m1r, k6, ssk, yo, k2.
Row 2 (ws): p3, ssp, p13, p2tog, p3.
Row 3: k2, k2tog, k6, m1l, k1, m1r, k6, ssk, k2.
Row 4: purl.
Row 5: k2, k2tog, k6, m1l, k1, m1r, k6, ssk, k2.
Row 6: purl.
Row 7: k2, k2tog, k6, m1l, k1, m1r, k6, ssk, k2.
Row 8: purl.

Repeat these 8 rows 5 more times, then work Rows 1 and 2. 7 buttonholes created on each side, work measures approximately 13" from the Ankle section, measured along the center increase ridge. Spats can easily be made shorter or taller by changing the number of Leg repeats.

rs: BO all sts.

Back Panel (Make 2):
CO 31 sts.
NOTE: For a wider calf, simply cast on additional stitches (odd number). Back panel is very stretchy and will accommodate many sizes.

Half-Twisted Rib Pattern:
Row 1: k3, *p1, ktbl* to last 4 sts, p1, k3.
Row 2: p3, *k1, ptbl* to last 4 sts, k1 p3.

Repeat these two rows until work measures 15", or length of front panel measured from the widest part of the foot to

the top edge (see schematic).
BO in pattern (knit the knits, purl the purls, passing the second stitch over the first).

FINISHING:
Weave in all ends.

Block front panel lightly if desired (the increases/decreases will create a natural foot/ankle shape).

Sew on 8 buttons to each edge of the two back panels, evenly spaced along the knit selvage edge (32 buttons total, or total number of buttonholes plus 4 for decoration). One button should be near the very top, one near the very bottom - see schematic.

Button back panels to front, leaving the bottom button undone. Smaller buttons may be used by sewing the buttonholes tighter with scrap yarn.

If using elastic: measure a length of elastic that will fit securely around your shoe. Sew this into a loop. Sew this to the underside of the foot, where the two plain rows were worked before the ankle section.

If using ribbon: thread a length of ribbon under your foot and up through the yo2 holes. Tie in a lovely bow.

Wear and enjoy!

Schematic

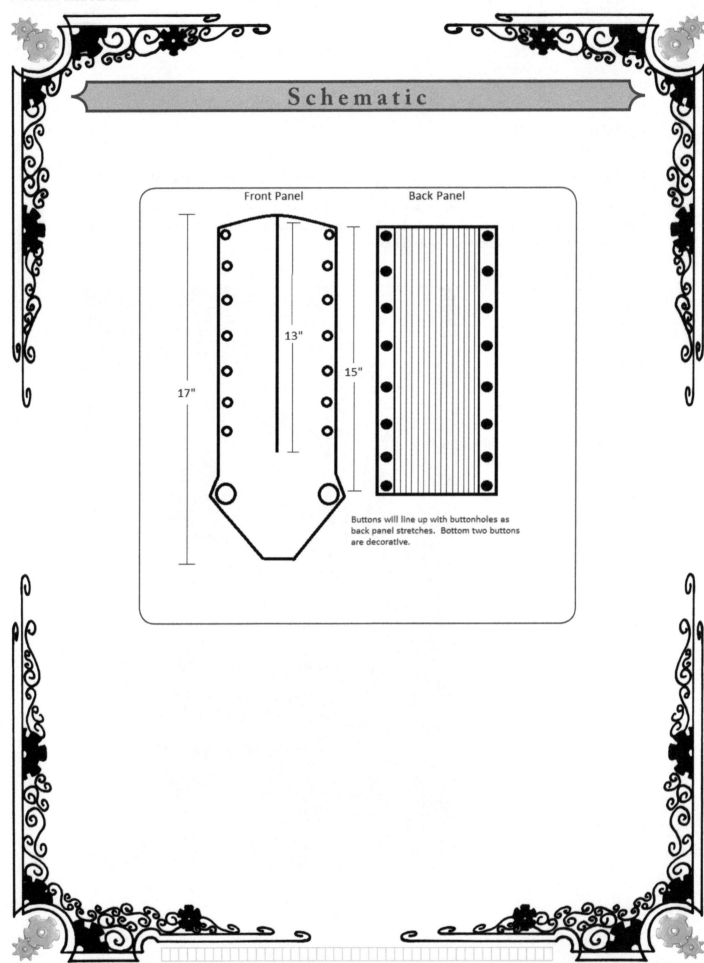

Front Panel

Back Panel

13"

15"

17"

Buttons will line up with buttonholes as back panel stretches. Bottom two buttons are decorative.

The Incandescent Cowl

By: Heidi Kunkel

DESCRIPTION:
A lacy cowl, knit flat, with gussets that flare around the bottom to flatter the shape of your neck. It is designed to button partway, left open at the bottom.

SPECIAL TECHNIQUES:
Buttonholes:
There are 6 buttonholes in this cowl - 2 on ws rows, and 4 on rs rows.

When working buttonholes on rs rows, work to the last four stitches, p1, yo, p2tog, k1. Do this on row 7 of the chart on your first two repeats, and row 5 of the chart on the final two

repeats.
When working buttonholes on ws rows, sl1, k2tog, yo, knit to end. Do this on your second garter stitch row after the cast on, and your last garter stitch row before the bind off.

A little glow, a little spark, a touch of radiant warmth. In the cool grey of the city, the dim, dusty workshop; or the smoke of the engine room, this charming cowl brings a welcome burst of light and energy. You may find yourself suddenly inspired to knit all through the wee hours of the night, making one for each of your friends. I'm sure Tesla would approve.

Gusset:

The gussets are worked in reverse stockinette framed between two knit stitches (one on either side), decreasing on either edge every right side row until only two purl stitches remain between the two knit stitches. This will occur when you're on Row 17, which will be Row 5 of your second repeat of the chart. I like using markers to separate out the gusset sections until I'm far enough into the pattern that it becomes obvious.

Row 1 (rs) and all rs rows: ssk, purl to 2 sts before marker, k2tog.
Row 2 and all ws rows: p1, knit to one stitch before marker, p1.

Once you have decreased to 4 stitches (2 purls between the knit stitches) you will just continue to work these 4 stitches as k1, p2, k1 on the rs between the lace sections.

FINISHED DIMENSIONS:
Circumference:
At top: 14½" (relaxed)
At base: 21½" (relaxed)
Height: 7½"

YARN AND YARDAGE:
Princess Sophia by Woolen Mill St. Yarns, http://christinamariepotter.etsy.com
100% merino; 400yds (366m) per 100g; light fingering weight
Color: Fishsticks & Custard, 1 skein

GAUGE:
Ball band gauge of chosen yarn: 33-40 sts = 4"
Knitted and blocked gauge:
In stockinette: 29 sts x 38 rows = 4"/10cm
One repeat of lace pattern: 2½" wide

NEEDLES AND NOTIONS:
One 24" size 4 US/3.5mm circular needle
Tapestry needle
8 stitch markers
6 small buttons (approximately 11mm suggested)

PATTERN NOTES:

This pattern is worked flat, and then buttons are sewn onto the edging of one side. There is a 4 stitch ribbed edging on either side that is not included in the chart. Reverse stockinette gussets at the bottom decrease into ribbing as the cowl progresses. Try to keep even tension on the selvedge stitches for a clean edge.

Pattern

Cast on: the cast on is worked with yarn held doubled. If long tail is your preferred method, a nice touch is to only double the yarn end that goes over your thumb. Don't double the strand that goes over your pointer finger.

Holding yarn doubled (refer to Pattern Notes), cast on 181 stitches as follows: CO 21, pm, CO 22, pm, CO 17, pm, CO 22, pm, CO 17, pm, CO 22, pm, CO 17, pm, CO 22, pm, CO 21. Drop second strand of yarn and continue pattern using a single strand.

Work 6 rows in garter stitch, slipping first stitch of each row purlwise, keeping in mind that if you've used the long tail cast on, you've already included the first row.

At the same time:
Work a buttonhole (refer to Special Techniques) at the start of the second garter row.

Begin working Row 1 of the lace chart and gusset as follows: sl1, p1, k1, p1, *work lace repeat, sm, work gusset (refer to Special Techniques), sm,* 4 times, work lace repeat once more, p1, k1, p1, k1. Continue working buttonholes, referring to Special Techniques for details.

Row 2 and all ws rows: sl1, k1, p1, k1, follow lace chart and gusset instructions across the row to the last 4 stitches, k1, p1, k1, p1.

Row 3 and all remaining rs rows: sl1 knitwise, p1, k1, p1, follow lace chart and gusset instructions across the row to the last 4 stitches, p1, k1, p1, k1.

You will finish decreasing the gusset stitches (leaving only k1, p2, k1 on the rs between lace repeats) when you're on Row 5 of the 2nd repeat of the lace pattern.

After working the remainder of that repeat (through row 12), work rows 1-12 of lace chart two more times for a total of 4 repeats, or until cowl is desired length.

Continuing the selvedge edge, work 6 rows of garter stitch, working the buttonhole at the beginning of the last (ws) garter row.

Hold yarn doubled and bind off.

FINISHING:
Weave in ends, and block very lightly taking care not to stretch out ribbing sections. I found it useful to stretch mine vertically while blocking, and to block it, wrong side up, into a rectangle with the gussets folded up away from the blocking board, as it's not something that can easily be blocked to only two dimensions.

Sew buttons opposite to buttonholes, wear and enjoy!

Chart

17	16	15	14	13	12	11	10	9	8	7	6	5	4	3	2	1	
																	12
	O			Λ		O	/	O		Λ		O		O			11
																	10
	O					O	Λ	O		Λ				O			9
																	8
	O			O	Λ	O	\	O		Λ				O			7
																	6
	O		O	Λ		O	/	O		Λ				O			5
																	4
	O			Λ		O	Λ	O						O			3
																	2
		O		Λ			O	/	O	Λ	O				O		1

Legend:

Symbol	Name	Description
(blank)	**knit**	knit stitch
O	**yo**	Yarn Over
Λ	**sl1 k2tog psso**	slip 1, k2tog, pass slip stitch over k2tog
/	**k2tog**	Knit two stitches together as one stitch
\	**ssk**	Slip one stitch as if to knit, Slip another stitch as if to knit. Insert left-hand needle into front of these 2 stitches and knit them together

The Schematic Sock

By: Aimee Skeers

DESCRIPTION:
A mid-calf sock knit from the toe up, with a flap heel and a knit-purl gear panel on the outside of the leg, these socks can be worn by both men and women. The mostly-stockinette pattern lends itself to resizing.

GARMENT DIMENSIONS:
Foot circumference: 7⅛"
Foot length: 9¼"
Leg circumference: 7⅛"

TO FIT BODY MEASUREMENTS:
Women's foot sized 7½

YARN AND YARDAGE:
Willow by Huckleberry Knits, http://huckleberryknits. etsy.com
80% BFL, 20% nylon; 420yds (384m) per 114g; fingering weight
Color: Limitless, 1 skein

Is there a hidden plan in the gears? With the Ladies always scheming or creating something, you can never be too sure. However, one thing is certain: these socks prove that tinkering is not just for the laboratory or engine room. Knit up these genius machinations and let people wonder what you are up to...

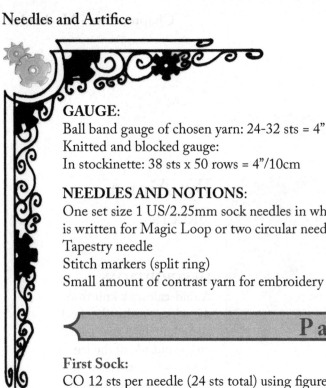

GAUGE:
Ball band gauge of chosen yarn: 24-32 sts = 4"
Knitted and blocked gauge:
In stockinette: 38 sts x 50 rows = 4"/10cm

NEEDLES AND NOTIONS:
One set size 1 US/2.25mm sock needles in whatever format you prefer for sock knitting. This pattern is written for Magic Loop or two circular needles.
Tapestry needle
Stitch markers (split ring)
Small amount of contrast yarn for embroidery

Pattern

First Sock:
CO 12 sts per needle (24 sts total) using figure-8 cast on or similar.
K one round.

Attach split ring stitch marker to the bottom right side of the stitches on the needle facing you. This marks the beginning of the round. The sts on the needle closest to you are instep sts, the sts on the needle further from you are sole sts.

Round 1: *k1, m1, k to 1 st before end of needle, m1, k1,* rep between * once more, for a total of 2 repeats. 4 sts increased.
Round 2: knit.

Repeat these two rounds until you have 68 sts total, 34 sts per needle.

Work in stst until sock measures 6½ inches from CO.

Begin gusset increases as follows:
Round 1: k across instep needle. On sole needle, k1, m1, k to 1 st before end of sole needle, m1, k1. 2 sts increased.
Round 2: knit.

Repeat these two rounds 12 times total. 24 sts increased.

Turn Heel:
K instep sts. On sole sts, k the 13 gusset sts, then turn heel as follows:

K 30 sts, w&t.

P 29 sts, w&t.

Knit to two sts before the previous wrapped st (one unwrapped st between each wrapped st), w&t. Continue in this manner until you have 10 unwrapped sts left.

K across heel sts, knitting the wraps together with their stitches.

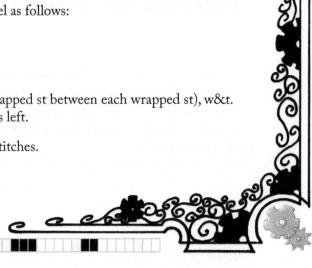

After knitting the last wrapped stitch together with its wrap, turn, sl1pwise and purl back, purling the wraps together with their stitches.

After purling the last wrapped stitch together with its wrap, turn.

Row 1: *sl1, k1,* repeat between * to last heel st, then ssk heel st together with first gusset st. Turn.
Row 2: sl1, p across to last heel st, then p2tog with first gusset st. Turn.
Repeat these two rows until all gusset sts are used up, ending with a rs (sl1, k1) row.

On the next row, pick up and knit 1 st between each needle to replace the sts lost during the heel turn.
Total stitches: 68

K 5 rounds.
On next round, k 23 sts, pm, work Row 1 of Gear Chart A, pm, k23.
Continue like this, working chart between markers, until chart is finished.
The chart tiles vertically, and can be knit as many times as wished if a longer sock is desired.
K 5 rounds.
Work in k2, p2 rib for 16 rounds.
BO.

Second Sock:
Work as first, but with the nearest needle to you as sole sts and the far needle as instep sts and working Gear Chart B. This places the gear panel on the correct side of the sock.

FINISHING:
Using chain stitch and contrast color, embroider around the edges of each purl section, outlining the gears.

Weave in ends, block and wear.

Charts

Chart A

Chart B

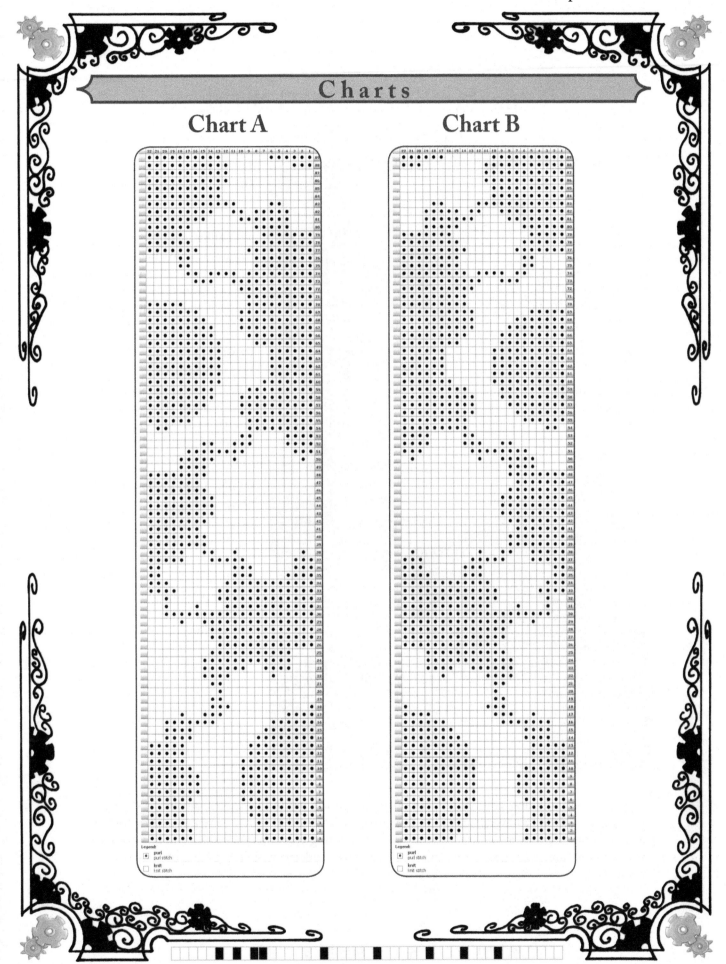

The Revolution Shrug
By: Katrina Elsaesser

DESCRIPTION:
Bias-knit shrug with fitted, ¾ length sleeves and a subtle pinstripe lace motif, all highlighted by a unique geometric construction. If desired, the spiral sleeve seams can be finished with lacing or a zipper, allowing the shrug to be converted to a shawl.

FINISHED DIMENSIONS:
Forearm circumference: 10"
Width across shoulders: 22"
Width across mid-back: 28"
Sleeve length (¾): 10"
Length at center-back: 13"

YARN AND YARDAGE:
80 10 10 Fingering by Sweet Basil Fibre Works, http://www.sweetbasil.ca
80% superwash merino, 10% cashmere, 10% nylon; 375yds (343m) per 100g; fingering weight
Color: Nomad, 2 skeins

It's the dawn of a new era: train tracks crisscrossing the nation, wheels of the steam engines turning, and always a new adventure on the horizon. And in that spirit, we've put quite a spin on a classic shrug. The swirling rows of lace and a fascinating construction ensure you'll never look at seams the same way again. We think it's a marvel of modern engineering - but of course, we're a bit... biased.

NOTE: The fabric of this shrug is very stretchy and can be blocked to fit a variety of sizes. Use the diagrams to determine which measurement on the garment is which prior to seaming, and adjust as needed.

EASE:
Block for desired ease, based on your measurements. Can be worn very fitted or slightly loose, as desired. Garment is modeled with 0-1" positive ease.

GAUGE:
This pattern is knit with a larger than standard needle size for the yarn weight.

Ball band gauge of chosen yarn: 26-32 sts = 4"
Knitted and blocked gauge:
In stockinette:
24 sts x 34 rows = 4"/10cm

In pattern (Right or Left Pinstripe Lace):
26 sts x 32 rows = 4"/10cm

NEEDLES AND NOTIONS:
One set size 5 US/3.75mm straight needles
Optional: zippers or ribbon for closing seams, if desired.

PATTERN NOTES:
Both row and stitch gauge are very important to achieve the proper garment proportions. Blocking can be used for size adjustments, if needed.

Pattern

Right Half:
Section A:
CO 3 sts
Work Setup Chart A once.
Total stitches: 25

Begin to work in Right Pinstripe Lace pattern, continuing to increase one stitch each row as in Setup Chart A.
Work all left edge stitches in stockinette until you've increased 6 sts, then begin working those stitches as a new repeat of the Right Pinstripe Lace.

Continue until you have 52 sts, ending with a wrong side row. Work should measure approximately 6 inches along straight edge (direction of knitting) and 10 inches along diagonal.

Section B:
Work 4 rows in pattern without increasing on the left edge.

Row 1 (rs): work in pattern until 1 stitch from the end of the row, m1k, k1.
Row 2 (ws): purl.
Row 3 (rs): work in pattern.
Row 4 (ws): purl.

Repeat these 4 rows 19 more times, for a total of 20 repeats, working stitches as additional lace repeats every time you've increased 6 stitches.

Total stitches: 72
Work should measure approximately 16½ inches along straight edge.

Section C:
Begin increasing on both right and left edges as follows. As before, incorporate additional lace repeats on either side after increasing a full 6 stitches.

Row 1 (rs): k1, m1k, work in pattern until 1 st from the end of the row, m1k, k1.
Row 2 (ws): purl.
Row 3 (rs): k1, m1k, work in pattern until the end of the row.
Row 4 (ws): purl.
Row 5 (rs): k1, m1k, work in pattern until 1 st from the end of the row, m1k, k1.
Row 6 (ws): purl until 3 sts from end of the row, m1p, p3.
Row 7 (rs): k1, m1k, work in pattern until the end of the row.
Row 8 (ws): purl.

Repeat these 8 rows 6 more times, for a total of 7 repeats. 14 sts increased on left edge, 35 sts increased on right edge.
Total stitches: 121
Work should measure approximately 16½ inches along left diagonal edge (Sections B and C).

Section D:
Row 1 (rs): k1, m1k, work in pattern until 3 sts from the end of the row, k2tog, k1.
Row 2 (ws): purl.
Row 3: k1, m1k, work in pattern until 3 sts from the end of the row, k2tog, k1.
Row 4: purl.
Row 5: k1, m1k, work in pattern until 3 sts from the end of the row, k2tog, k1.
Row 6: p3, p2tog, purl until 3 sts from end of the row, m1p, p3.
Row 7: k1, m1k, work in pattern until 3 sts from the end of the row, k2tog, k1.
Row 8: purl.

Increases and decreases are paired, so the stitch total remains 121.

Work should measure approximately 11 inches along right diagonal edge (Sections C and D).

Section E:
Row 1 (rs): k1, ssk, work in pattern until 3 sts from the end of the row, k2tog, k1.
Row 2 (ws): purl.
Row 3: k1, ssk, work in pattern until 3 sts from the end of the row, k2tog, k1.
Row 4: purl.
Row 5: k1, ssk, work in pattern until 3 sts from the end of the row, k2tog, k1.
Row 6: p3, p2tog, purl until 5 sts from end of the row, ssp, p3.
Row 7: k1, ssk, work in pattern until 3 sts from the end of the row, k2tog, k1.
Row 8: purl.

Repeat these 8 rows until 5 sts remain.

Next row (rs): k2tog, k1, ssk.
ws: purl.
rs: sl1, k2tog, psso.

Pull yarn through remaining stitch to bind off.

Work should measure approximately 13 inches along right diagonal and approximately 14 inches along left diagonal.

Right Half of shrug is complete. Begin Left Half.

Left Half:

Section A:

CO 3 sts

Work Setup Chart B once. Total stitches: 25

Begin to work in Left Pinstripe Lace pattern, continuing to increase one stitch each row as in Setup Chart B.

Work all right edge stitches in stockinette until you've increased 6 sts, then begin working those stitches as a new repeat of the Left Pinstripe Lace.

Continue until you have 52 sts, ending with a wrong side row. Work should measure approximately 6 inches along straight edge (direction of knitting) and 10 inches along diagonal.

Section B:

Work 4 rows in pattern without increasing on right edge.

Row 1 (rs): k1, m1k, work in pattern until the end of the row.

Row 2 (ws): purl.

Row 3 (rs): work in pattern.

Row 4 (ws): purl.

Repeat these 4 rows 19 more times, for a total of 20 repeats, working stitches as additional lace repeats every time you increase 6 stitches.

Total stitches: 72

Work should measure approximately 16½ inches along straight edge.

Section C:

Begin increasing on both right and left edges as follows. As before, incorporate additional lace repeats on either side after you've increased a full 6 stitches.

Row 1 (rs): k1, m1k, work in pattern until 1 st from the end of the row, m1k, k1.

Row 2 (ws): purl.

Row 3: work in pattern until 1 st from the end of the row, m1k, k1.

Row 4: purl.

Row 5: k1, m1k, work in pattern until 1 st from the end of the row, m1k, k1.

Row 6: p3, m1p, purl to the end of the row.

Row 7: work in pattern until 1 st from the end of the row, m1k, k1.

Row 8: purl.

Repeat these 8 rows 6 more times, for a total of 7 repeats. 14 sts increased on right edge, 35 sts increased on left edge.

Total stitches: 121

Work should measure approximately 16½ inches along left diagonal edge (Sections B and C).

Section D:
Row 1 (rs): k1, ssk, work in pattern until 1 st from the end of the row, m1k, k1.
Row 2 (ws): purl.
Row 3: k1, ssk, work in pattern until 1 st from the end of the row, m1k, k1.
Row 4: purl.
Row 5: k1, ssk, work in pattern until 1 st from the end of the row, m1k, k1.
Row 6: p3, m1p, purl until 5 sts from the end of the row, ssp, p3.
Row 7: k1, ssk, work in pattern until 1 st from the end of the row, m1k, k1.
Row 8: purl.
Increases and decreases are paired, so the stitch total remains 121.

Work should measure approximately 11 inches along left diagonal edge (Sections C and D).

Section E:
Row 1 (rs): k1, ssk, work in pattern until 3 sts from the end of the row, k2tog, k1.
Row 2 (ws): purl.
Row 3: k1, ssk, work in pattern until 3 sts from the end of the row, k2tog, k1.
Row 4: purl.
Row 5: k1, ssk, work in pattern until 3 sts from the end of the row, k2tog, k1.
Row 6: p3, p2tog, purl until 5 sts from end of the row, ssp, p3.
Row 7: k1, ssk, work in pattern until 3 sts from the end of the row, k2tog, k1.
Row 8: purl.
Repeat these 8 rows until 5 sts remain.

Next row (rs): k2tog, k1, ssk
ws: purl.
rs: sl1, k2tog, psso.

Pull yarn through remaining stitch to bind off.

Work should measure approximately 13 inches along left diagonal and approximately 14 inches along right diagonal.

FINISHING:

Weave in ends and block both halves to the measurements on the schematic. You can adjust for your own measurements, but make sure the matching seams - indicated on the schematic in matching colored lines - are equal.

Seam center back along matching edges. Sew spiral sleeve seams as indicated on the schematic (match the two colored lines), beginning sewing at the forearm (10" edge) and working towards the armpit. Make sure the right sides are facing outward.

Alternately, you may finish the spiral sleeve seams by lacing with ribbon, or applying a zipper or other closure. This enables the shrug to also be worn as a shawl, and adds decorative interest.

Charts

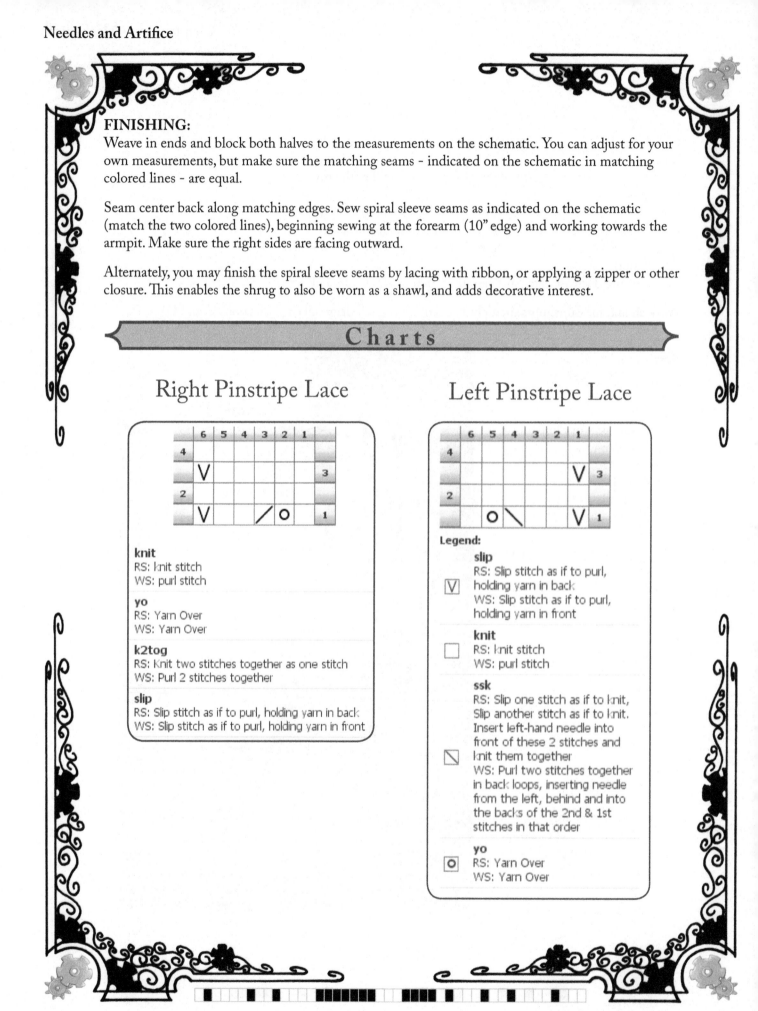

Right Pinstripe Lace

knit
RS: knit stitch
WS: purl stitch

yo
RS: Yarn Over
WS: Yarn Over

k2tog
RS: Knit two stitches together as one stitch
WS: Purl 2 stitches together

slip
RS: Slip stitch as if to purl, holding yarn in back
WS: Slip stitch as if to purl, holding yarn in front

Left Pinstripe Lace

Legend:

slip
V RS: Slip stitch as if to purl, holding yarn in back
WS: Slip stitch as if to purl, holding yarn in front

knit
☐ RS: knit stitch
WS: purl stitch

ssk
◩ RS: Slip one stitch as if to knit, Slip another stitch as if to knit. Insert left-hand needle into front of these 2 stitches and knit them together
WS: Purl two stitches together in back loops, inserting needle from the left, behind and into the backs of the 2nd & 1st stitches in that order

yo
◉ RS: Yarn Over
WS: Yarn Over

Setup Chart A

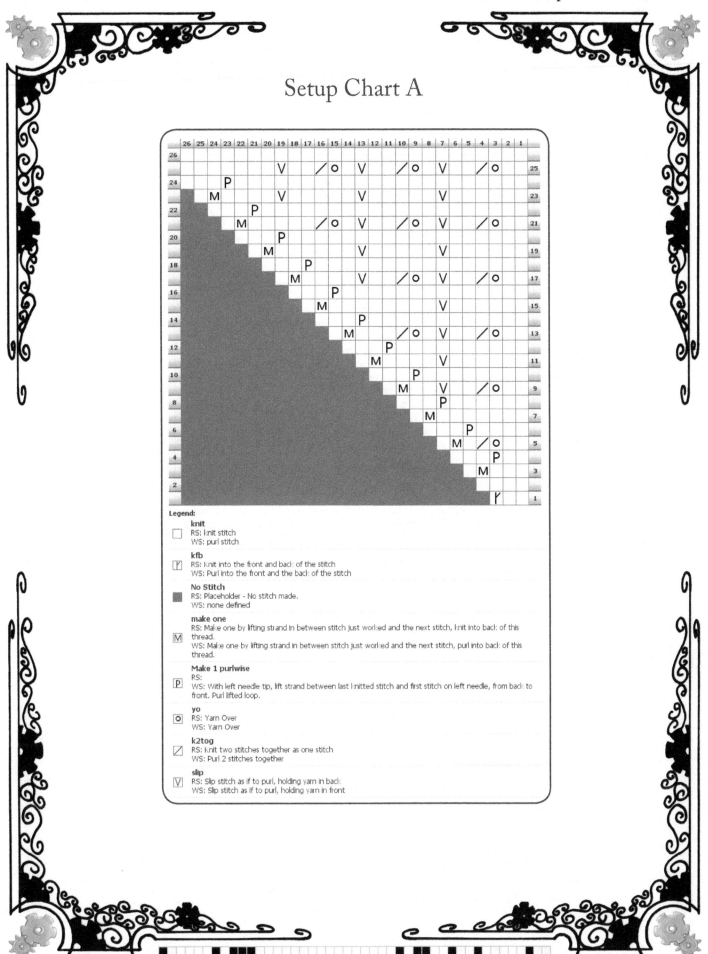

Legend:

knit
☐ RS: Knit stitch
WS: purl stitch

kfb
Ⅴ RS: Knit into the front and back of the stitch
WS: Purl into the front and the back of the stitch

No Stitch
▨ RS: Placeholder - No stitch made.
WS: none defined

make one
Ⅿ RS: Make one by lifting strand in between stitch just worked and the next stitch, knit into back of this thread.
WS: Make one by lifting strand in between stitch just worked and the next stitch, purl into back of this thread.

Make 1 purlwise
Ⲣ RS:
WS: With left needle tip, lift strand between last knitted stitch and first stitch on left needle, from back to front. Purl lifted loop.

yo
Ⲟ RS: Yarn Over
WS: Yarn Over

k2tog
╱ RS: Knit two stitches together as one stitch
WS: Purl 2 stitches together

slip
Ⅴ RS: Slip stitch as if to purl, holding yarn in back
WS: Slip stitch as if to purl, holding yarn in front

Setup Chart B

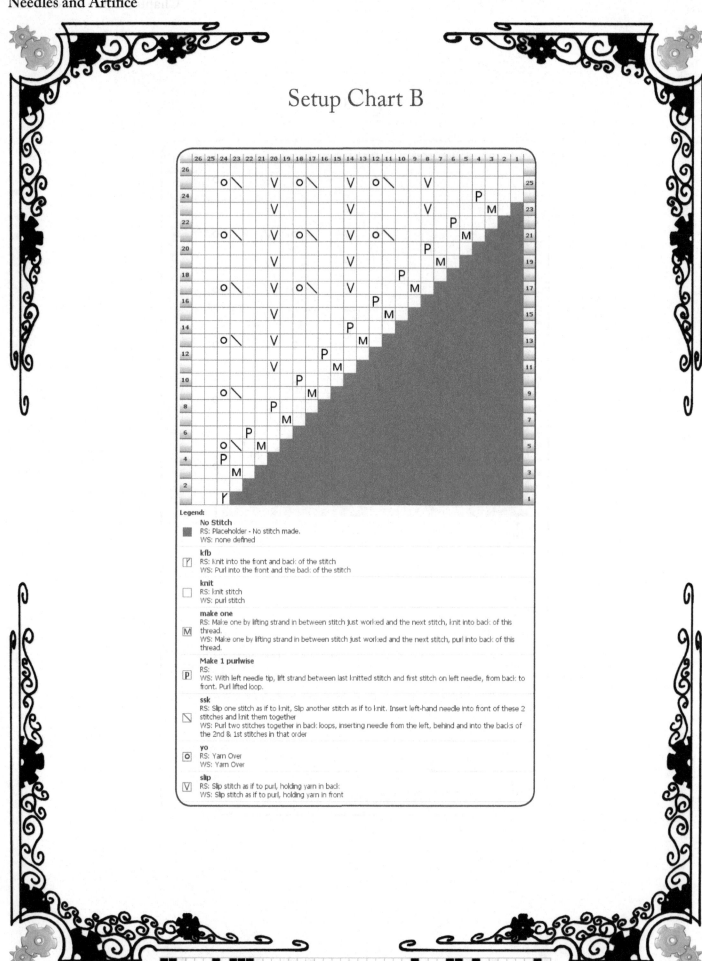

Legend:

No Stitch
RS: Placeholder - No stitch made.
WS: none defined

kfb
RS: Knit into the front and back of the stitch
WS: Purl into the front and the back of the stitch

knit
RS: Knit stitch
WS: purl stitch

make one
M
RS: Make one by lifting strand in between stitch just worked and the next stitch, knit into back of this thread.
WS: Make one by lifting strand in between stitch just worked and the next stitch, purl into back of this thread.

Make 1 purlwise
P
RS:
WS: With left needle tip, lift strand between last knitted stitch and first stitch on left needle, from back to front. Purl lifted loop.

ssk
RS: Slip one stitch as if to knit, Slip another stitch as if to knit. Insert left-hand needle into front of these 2 stitches and knit them together
WS: Purl two stitches together in back loops, inserting needle from the left, behind and into the backs of the 2nd & 1st stitches in that order

yo
RS: Yarn Over
WS: Yarn Over

slip
RS: Slip stitch as if to purl, holding yarn in back
WS: Slip stitch as if to purl, holding yarn in front

Schematic

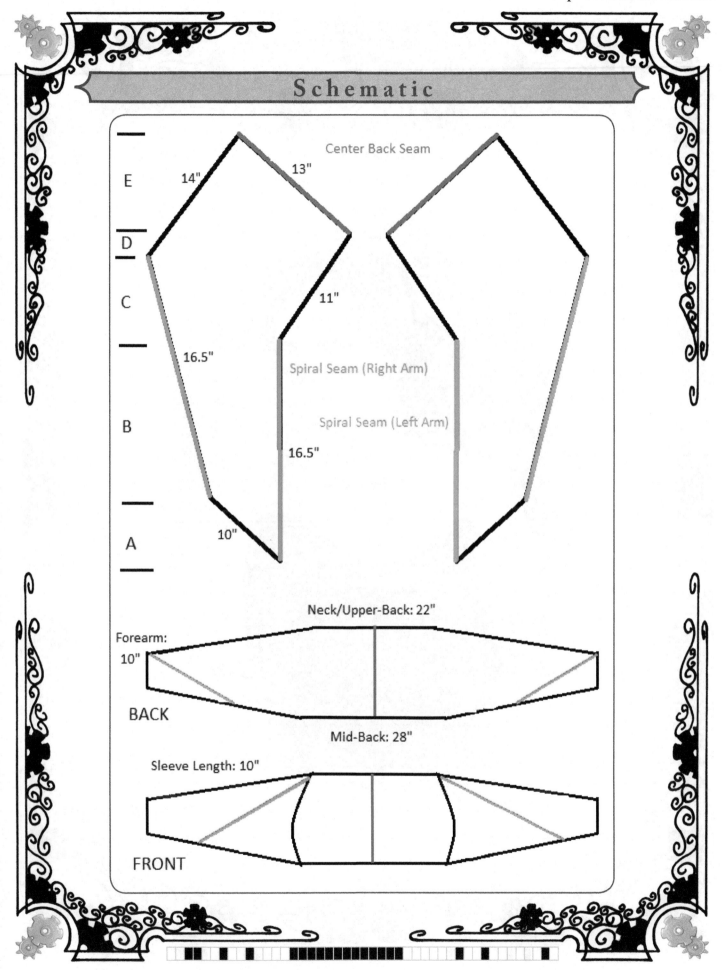

Center Back Seam

E

14" 13"

D

C 11"

16.5"

Spiral Seam (Right Arm)

B

Spiral Seam (Left Arm)

16.5"

A 10"

Neck/Upper-Back: 22"

Forearm:

10"

BACK

Mid-Back: 28"

Sleeve Length: 10"

FRONT

Chapter Two

In which both secrets and ankles are revealed

Alyssa Rynne's brooch chimed at an especially inopportune moment. She sighed inwardly, reached past the Second Lieutenant of the Royal Navy for a pen and paper, and jotted down the coded message. Her brow furrowed as she wrote, and her companion frowned in concern.

"What is wrong, dear Alyssa? I've never seen you looking less than serene." He pushed himself up on one elbow and rested a hand on her shoulder. Alyssa finished her note-taking and bestowed a soft smile upon the gentleman.

"It seems a dear friend is in trouble, my darling. I fear our time will be cut short today. My sincerest apologies, but this is rather urgent and my time is limited." She rested a hand on either side of his face and pressed a kiss to his forehead. Another smile, and she was moving away from him to her desk. "My servants will see you out."

"But Miss Alyssa!" he protested. "When shall I see you again?"

Alyssa threw him a wink back over her shoulder. "Leave your card at the door, darling, and I will see when our schedules synchronize again." She sat down at her desk and began the laborious process

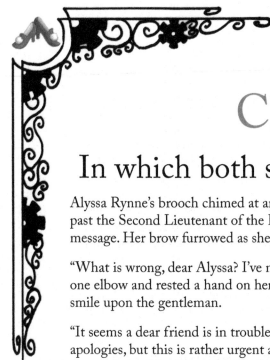

Alyssa Rynne was a courtesan and world traveler, who often provided romantic advice to the Ladies. She spent years traveling the world, enjoying the company of men of many countries, before choosing Shanghai as her home. The international community of dignitaries in Shanghai was much the richer because of her. Lonely politicians and military men, far from home and family, opened up like flowers in her warm glow and shared secrets of both a personal and professional tenor. Alyssa, being intelligent as well as beautiful, collected these secrets and passed them to the appropriate contacts for a price. Her dear friends, The Ladies of Mischief, often received coded messages from Alyssa, providing them with key information at just the right time to positively impact their endeavors. Her other messages, containing stories of her conquests, kept even the most forward Ladies blushing.

of canceling her social engagements for the day. She had been expecting a visit from Kitty the following day for tea, however this new emergency meant that the visit would be happening in a few short hours instead. The Second Lieutenant was leaving now, so next she wrote a letter expressing her regret that she must miss tea with the Italian Ambassador, followed by a note to the Japanese Ambassador to let him know she would have to miss dinner. Alyssa reflected that it would make her life a great deal easier if her friends could manage to schedule their emergencies. She chuckled quietly, as she imagined Anna's datebook entry for today's events, "22/7/1885: Crash Dirigible." A quick glance at the clock told her she had a few hours before she was needed for anything else, so she opened the hidden compartment at the back of her desk and removed the ledger that contained the other reason she found her social circle so engaging. Men loved her company and especially loved to unburden themselves with her. Alyssa

loved their company as well, and afterwards enjoyed sharing useful information with her network of contacts. Those contacts were most appreciative.

Some hours later, Alyssa had just ordered tea when she heard a loud pounding, prompting her to smile. There was only one person who would knock so aggressively on her delicately carved wooden door. She rose to greet her stranded friend.

"Oh, Anna!" The somewhat grimy redhead found herself enveloped in a fierce, jasmine-scented hug. "Are you all right? We heard about the crash when the message from Joanna went through. Let me look at you!" In a swirl of silks, Alyssa stood back to hold Anna at arm's length and look her up and down. Her brow furrowed. Anna's lips quirked.

"What, Alyssa? Are you shocked that I managed to go through a crash-landing without looking like it, or are you still disgruntled that my standard countenance looks like it's been through a crash-landing?" Anna grinned as Alyssa took a step back and crossed pale arms.

"I just think that a woman of your age and bearing would look simply marvelous in a silk gown, cut low in the front and very fitted through the bodice..." Alyssa's eyes glazed over slightly, clearly designing the perfect outfit in her mind. Anna sighed. If she let this go, Alyssa would be on about it for hours and nothing would get done. Drastic measures, then.

"Alyssa, have I introduced you to Kristoff Von Boltenstein?" Upon hearing the name Alyssa jolted immediately out of her daydream and turned sharp, appraising eyes on Kristoff. Kristoff felt slightly uneasy at that gaze. He felt like he was being added up and he wasn't sure if the sum would be sufficient. After a moment Alyssa presented him with a sunny smile and extended her hand.

"Ah, Kristoff. We've heard so much about you. Our Anna hasn't been running you too ragged, has she?" Alyssa's eyes twinkled as Kristoff took her hand and bowed deeply over it. He felt Alyssa would appreciate the courtesy, while Anna would probably punch him if he tried it with her.

"Miss Alyssa. It's an honor to meet you. Thank you so very much for allowing us to drop in on your..." Kristoff trailed off, looking around the room properly for the first time and taking in the décor. Chaise lounges abounded. Sumptuous swaths of silks hung from the walls and draped from the ceiling. Classical paintings of men and women in various states of undress adorned any part of the wall not occupied by fabric. It seemed like everywhere he looked, there was something that suggested intimacy and...other things. He swallowed. "In your boudoir," he managed to finish without his voice going too squeaky.

Alyssa laughed richly. "But of course, my dear gentleman! Anna is one of my Ladies, and we all help each other out. And my dear Kitty! What a great stroke of luck that you were nearby to pick up our fallen Anna." Alyssa and Caldonia exchanged a long hug. "But wherever are your men?"

Caldonia smiled with a touch of sadness. "I've sent them home with my botanical samples. After hearing Anna's story, I feel that I must continue to assist her in this adventure. Without distraction."

"What a kind gesture. And though I am dying to hear Anna's story, I have very serious information that I must share with you first. Please, be seated." Kristoff perched on the edge of an ottoman. Alyssa barely managed to keep from wincing as Anna sprawled across an armchair and stuck her booted

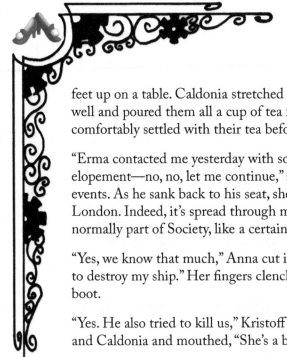

feet up on a table. Caldonia stretched out luxuriously on a large chaise. Their hostess took a seat as well and poured them all a cup of tea from a delicate porcelain pot. She waited until they were all comfortably settled with their tea before she continued.

"Erma contacted me yesterday with some very disturbing information. It seems that news of your elopement—no, no, let me continue," she added as Kristoff came to his feet to protest this version of events. As he sank back to his seat, she went on, "News of your rumored elopement has spread across London. Indeed, it's spread through most of Society... And it's even spread to those who are not normally part of Society, like a certain Klaus Von Boltenstein."

"Yes, we know that much," Anna cut in, venom sizzling in her voice. "He's the one who hired pirates to destroy my ship." Her fingers clenched and unclenched just above the handle of the knife in her boot.

"Yes. He also tried to kill us," Kristoff added, rolling his eyes at Anna just a little. He turned to Alyssa and Caldonia and mouthed, "She's a bit touchy about the ship."

Alyssa covered her mouth to politely hide a smirk, then took a sip of her tea before she continued. "Yes. Well, the issue we're facing is that Klaus wants you dead for a specific reason. He intends to replace you in Society. You and Anna both."

Anna frowned and sat forward. "Me? How does he plan to do that? If he wants to kidnap me he probably shouldn't have had my ship blown up."

Alyssa shook her head. "No. That's not what he intends. He has obtained photographs of you, and according to Erma, he has constructed a clockwork doppelganger." She set her teacup down carefully and folded her hands in her lap. "Once you and Kristoff are dead, he intends to take your places using this 'Clockwork Anna.' She is very lifelike, I understand, and completely under his control."

All four of them shuddered and were quiet for a moment. Kristoff broke the silence. "I must return to England immediately and put a stop to this." His voice was quiet, but firm and full of resolve. Anna snorted loudly.

"'I' must return? What's this 'I' horsebobbles?" she demanded. "If you think you're going anywhere without me, you're a dolt. He destroyed. My. Ship!" The last word was punctuated by the THUMP of her boots coming down off the table and impacting the floor. "I said I was going to track down your brother and make him pay. I still stand by that." She grabbed her tea and downed the contents in one angry gulp.

A fetching servant girl silently approached Alyssa with a telegram. Alyssa read it, nodded sharply, then gazed directly into Anna's eyes.

"I think you will find that neither of you are going without me and Kitty, as well. And Cora, as it is her personal high-speed airship that will take you to England. She'll be here in the morning." She raised the telegram envelope. "When her brooch went off, she deduced your path. She has already begun the journey here. Now, then, you'll be staying here overnight. Kristoff, you'll find a suite down this hall. You may bathe and avail yourself of any of the clothes in the wardrobe. I'll have dinner sent to you. Kitty, you can have the suite just beyond this door. As for you, Anna..." Alyssa turned

her piercing gaze on the more scruffy of the trio and grabbed the back of her collar. "You are taking a bath before you sleep in any of my beds. Come along." Anna was dragged from the sitting room, leaving a perplexed Kristoff and a smiling Caldonia behind.

"Right," Alyssa said once they were safely ensconced in the bathing room. Her stern demeanor dropped and her face lit up with curiosity. "How has it been with Kristoff? Also, I meant what I said about the bath, so strip." Anna sighed and started undoing buttons.

"Good? Terrible? I don't know!" she wailed, dropping her jacket to the floor. "I don't know what to do! I knit the thing you suggested--" she waved a hand at the leather bundle she'd brought with her "-- and it even survived the crash, but I still don't know what he wants." Anna slumped into the bathtub with a sullen splash and blew bubbles under the surface for a moment.

"Wash. With soap." Alyssa allowed Anna to scrub for a moment. "Tell me what you mean, you don't know what he wants?"

Anna sighed and lathered up one arm. "I mean... Sometimes he seems like he wants to touch me, but then he realizes what's happening and he pulls his hands back like I'll burn him." She lathered the other arm now, only slightly aggressively. "He makes me breakfast and tea, but he always remains perfectly gentlemanly at all times. Never inappropriate. He never even swears, for stitches' sake!" Both arms were rinsed with slightly more force than required, and Alyssa leaned back out of splashing distance. "I just don't know what to do," Anna repeated. "I've never done this before."

"What? Bathed? Yes, I had imagined." Alyssa dodged the sponge and held up her hands in surrender. "I jest!" She smiled warmly and settled

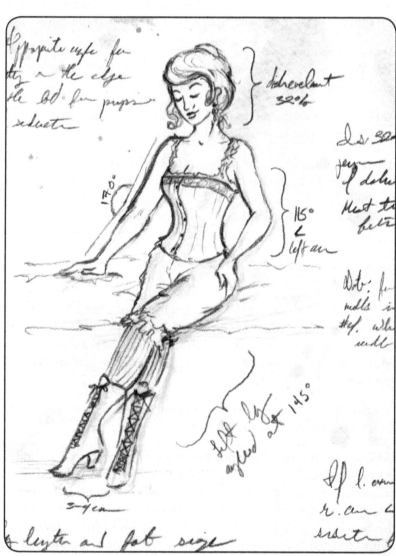

back down. "I think part of your issue is that you have no idea what your seduction style is. Wash your hair."

"Seduction style?" Anna asked from under a mound of shampoo. "There's more than one?"

Alyssa laughed. "Oh, goodness yes! There are dozens! It can be quite a chore to learn them all, but you don't need to do that. You just need one that will work for you."

Anna frowned. "What do you suggest?"

Alyssa pondered for a moment, then brightened. "Just think upon The Ladies of Mischief. Our dear friends employ several seduction styles that might suit you. Kitty, for example, is coy. She tells gentlemen that she's interested using her eyes. They flock to her with just a few looks."

Anna attempted this. Alyssa shook her head. "No, dear. That's a glare. Perhaps you could try a commanding style, like Cora? She simply orders her gentlemen into her bed. They are usually quite eager to obey."

Anna bit her lower lip. "I don't want to make him uncomfortable. If I give him an order and he's uninterested, I don't want him to feel like he doesn't have a choice."

Alyssa nodded. "That's understandable. Hm... I don't think Theo's method would work for you. She's rather elusive, and that's not helpful." She held out a towel to Anna as the redhead exited the tub, dripping all over the floor. "And our dear Erma, though she wouldn't lack for male company if she wished it, is simply unaware of her clothing and bearing much of the time." Alyssa's eyes glinted. "I could always teach you glamor! That is my specialty, after all. Here, you're dry and dressed. Now let me comb your hair."

Anna wrapped a dressing gown around herself grumpily and flopped down on a chair. "No, thank you. Glamor is not something I find interesting. I don't think any of the Ladies have a style that will work for me." She picked up a cup and examined the contents, hoping perhaps it would have some helpful information. It only contained tea. Anna sighed and took a sip.

"Well, then. You'll just have to find one for yourself, won't you? There, you're all done. Unless you want to consider some of my cosmetics?" Alyssa let the question hover in the air for a moment. It might happen this time. Anna might actually take her up on it...

"No! No. He needs to be able to recognize me." Anna snorted. "Maybe we could smear some coal dust on my face?" She couldn't see the look on Alyssa's face, but she felt certain it was an expression of disgust. "At any rate, it wouldn't help my confidence." She looked down at her teacup and tightened her hand on it. She nodded, sharply. "Right. Time to do this thing." Anna downed her tea in one gulp, then stood and strode out of the room. It was a stride more suited to someone heading out to do battle, but she didn't know any other way to stride.

Alyssa pursed her lips and stared off into space for a moment. "'Time to do this thing.' Hm... I suppose that would be a determined seduction style," she mused to herself. "Somewhat unusual, but it might work."

Anna continued her warrior's walk through the sitting area and down the hall, slowing when she approached the door of Kristoff's guest suite. She paused outside it for a moment, then jumped up and down in place a few times. "Right. Let's do this. Best to get it over with," she said to herself. "And if I say that often enough, maybe I'll even believe it," she muttered. She removed her dressing gown to expose the knitted lingerie set she'd worked on in the evenings in her cabin back on the Arcadia at Alyssa's suggestion.

She pulled her shoulders back and tipped her chin up. It was now or never, and she'd wouldn't forgive herself if it ended up being never. Anna flung the door open and stepped inside.

"Kristoff. I'm incredibly attracted to you and I want to know if you feel the same way. I know this might be a little sudden with me in the chemise and all, but I didn't want to wait any longer. Oh, bobbles. You're not even in this room." Anna scowled at the empty room and turned her eyes toward the closed door that she presumed led to the en suite washroom. Kristoff really had terrible timing, she reflected. Ah, well. She'd just have to come up with another plan of attack. She shut the door behind her and moved to the bed. Her nose wrinkled as she tried to figure out how this was supposed to work. Should she lay on her side? Stomach? Back? Lounge somehow? Oh curses, this was awkward. Anna decided to sit on the edge of the bed, spine ramrod straight, foot tapping impatiently.

That was how Kristoff found her when he opened the door to his guest bedroom, wrapped in a dressing gown and toweling his hair dry. They both froze. The towel slipped, forgotten, from his hands and landed on the floor with a soft whump.

"A-A-A-A-Anna?" he managed to squeak out as a blush heated his cheeks. "What? How? Why? What?"

Anna took a deep breath. "I care about you deeply and want to snog you right now," she tried to say, but her mouth went a little too fast and it came out more like, "Icaroutyoudeewannasnogrinow." She bit her lip and slapped herself upside the head. "Sorry, I'm so nervous right now I'm about to vomit. Oh, bobbles, I suppose talking about vomiting really isn't appealing. Curses! This isn't going properly at all so I'm going to really try and say it properly this time." She met his eyes and squared her shoulders. "Kristoff. I love you. Kiss me."

Kristoff stared, agog. His brain scrambled to understand what had just happened, but it was having a serious amount of difficulty when she was sitting there in that outfit. He closed his eyes and shook his head, trying to clear it. "Um. I'm sorry, what? Because it sounded like you just said you love me."

Anna lifted her chin. "I did. And I do. Are you going to do something about it?" Her eyes glinted, daring him to join her on the bed.

Kristoff ran a hand through his hair and sagged against the doorframe. "You... You really... I never thought..." Come on, brain! Stop getting distracted by those legs!

Anna looked away, but not before he saw the hurt in her eyes. "If you don't want me here, I'll go." She started to stand, and finally his body was capable of actual movement, and he crossed the room and grabbed her shoulder. She looked back up at him, biting her lower lip, and a gentle smile played across his face.

"I never thought... But I certainly hoped." Kristoff cupped her cheek in his hand. Anna's face split into a huge grin, and she turned to face him and wrapped her arms around his neck.

"Come here, you dolt," she said, and pulled his lips to hers. It was fiery and fierce, just like her. Kristoff hoped it would never end, but in the jumble of limbs and touching, he felt the back of his knees hit the edge of the bed and he had to sit down or fall down. Anna looked down at him, her face flushed, and began to sit down next to him.

"Anna, are you sure? I love you, I do, but this... If people find out, it might make things worse for you." He thought back to their earlier conversation about honor, those weeks ago when she first brought him aboard the Arcadia. Good Lord, he'd certainly never expected that this would happen!

Anna stood still for a moment, pondering his words. He did have a bit of a point, she had to admit... A wicked grin crossed her face, and she slowly pulled the straps of knitted chemise down over her shoulders and held it in place for a moment. She raised an eyebrow at the look on his face.

"I won't tell anyone if you won't."

The chemise slithered to the floor.

The Trials and Tribulations
Chemise and Bloomers

By: Aimee Skeers

DESCRIPTION:

Worked in the round from the bottom-up, the chemise features a scoop neck and set-in sleeve armholes trimmed with a lace cap. Bust gussets allow an attractive fit above an empire waist cinched with ribbon and a lace skirt that falls to the hips. The bloomers are worked bottom-up in the round, with rear gussets to allow a comfortable and flattering fit for the back and a ribbed waistband cinched with ribbon for a secure fit.

The path to romance may be fraught with ups and downs, but this cunning boudoir set is sure to smooth any bumps along the way. Sweet, playful and approachable: a winning combination in love and knitwear.

SPECIAL TECHNIQUES:
Kitchener Stitch, 3-Needle Bind Off.

FINISHED DIMENSIONS:
Bust: 32 (38, 42, 46, 50, 54)"
Hips: 38 (44, 48, 52, 56, 60)"
Thigh: 20 (22, 24, 26, 28, 30)"

TO FIT BODY MEASUREMENTS:
Bust: 32 (38, 42, 46, 50, 54)"
Hips: 32 (38, 42, 46, 50, 54)"
Thigh: 20 (22, 24, 26, 28, 30)"

EASE:
Chemise: No ease
Bloomers: 6" of positive ease at hip, none at thigh

YARN AND YARDAGE:
Prestige by Evermore Studios, http://www.evermorestudios.etsy.com
100% superwash BFL; 438yds (400m) per 100g; fingering weight
Chemise:
Color: Really Red, 2 (2, 3, 3, 4, 4) skeins
Bloomers:
Color: Gypsy, 2 (2, 3, 3, 4, 4) skeins

GAUGE:
Ball band gauge of chosen yarn: 28-36 sts = 4"
In stockinette:
On size 2 needles: 32 sts x 44 rows = 4"/10cm
On size 5 needles: 29 sts x 33 rows = 4"/10cm
On size 8 needles: 22 sts x 30 rows = 4"/10cm

In Pattern:
On size 8 needles: 1 pattern repeat = 2¼"

NEEDLES AND NOTIONS:
24", 32" and 40" size 2 US/2.75mm circular needles
24", 32", and 40" size 5 US/3.75mm circular needles
32" size 6 US/4mm circular needle
32" size 7 US/4.5mm circular needle
24" and 32" size 8 US/5mm circular needles
Tapestry needle
4 (4½, 5, 5½, 6, 6½) yards of ribbon, to be cut to lengths appropriate to tie in a bow around the underbust, waist and thighs
A crochet hook one mm size smaller than your medium needle (size 5 in pattern)
Stitch markers

Pattern

Chemise Body:
CO 288 (342, 378, 414, 450, 486) sts with size 8 needle and 32" cable.
Join in the round, knit 1 row, pm.
Begin working Lace Chart.

Work these four rows until work measures 4 (4½, 5, 5½, 6, 6½) inches from beginning. Switch to size 7 needles and continue in pattern until work measures 8 (9, 10, 11, 12, 13) inches from beginning.

Switch to size 6 needles and work in pattern until work measures 11 (12, 13½, 14½, 16, 17) inches from beginning.

On next round:
Size 32: *k1, k2tog,* repeat between * 96 times total.

Size 38: k1, *k2tog, k2,* repeat between * 18 times total, *k2tog, k1,* repeat between * 65 times total, *k2tog, k2,* repeat between * 18 times total, until 2 sts from end, k2tog.

Size 42: k1, *k2tog, k2,* repeat between * 30 times total, *k2tog, k1,* repeat between * 45 times total, *k2tog, k2,* repeat between * 30 times total, until 2 sts from end, k2tog.

Size 46: k1, *k2tog, k2,* repeat between * 42 times total, *k2tog, k1,* repeat between * 25 times total, *k2tog, k2,* repeat between * 42 times total, until 2 sts from end, k2tog.

Size 50: k1, *k2tog, k2,* repeat between * 54 times total, *k2tog, k1,* repeat between * 5 times total, *k2tog, k2,* repeat between * 54 times total, until 2 sts from end, k2tog.

Size 54: k1, *k2tog, k2,* repeat between * 42 times total, *k2tog, k1,* repeat between * 49 times total, *k2tog, k2,* repeat between * 42 times total, until 2 sts from end, k2tog.

96 (102, 106, 110, 114, 134) sts decreased. Total stitches: 192 (240, 272, 304, 336, 352)

Switch to size 2 needles and work in 2x2 rib for ¾".

On next row, work as follows: *k2, yo, p2tog, k2, p2,* repeat between * to end marker. Work in 2x2 rib until rib measures 1½".
Switch to size 5 needles.

Bust Shaping:
K32 (40, 45, 50, 56, 58) sts, place first bust gusset marker, k32 (40, 46, 52, 56, 60) sts, place second bust gusset marker, k32 (40, 45, 50, 56, 58) sts, place arm hole marker, k32 (40, 45, 50, 56, 58) sts, place first back shoulder gusset marker, k32 (40, 46, 52, 56, 60) sts, place second back shoulder gusset marker, k to end.

End of round marker marks first arm hole.

Total stitches front and back (each): 96 (120, 136, 152, 168, 176)

Begin Increases:
Round 1: k to first bust marker, m1, sm, k to second bust marker, sm, m1, knit to first back gusset marker (ignoring arm hole marker), m1, sm, k to second back gusset marker, sm, m1, k to end. 4 sts increased.

Round 2: knit.
Round 3: knit.

Round 4: k to first bust marker, m1, sm, k to second bust marker, sm, m1, k to end. 2 sts increased.

Round 5: knit.
Round 6: knit.

Repeat these rounds 5 (5, 4, 4, 4, 5) more times, for a total of 6 (6, 5, 5, 5, 6) repeats.

Work Round 1 another 1 (0, 1, 0, 0, 1) time.

40 (36, 34, 30, 30, 40) sts increased.

Total stitches: 232 (276, 306, 334, 366, 392)
Front stitches: 122 (144, 158, 172, 188, 200)
Back stitches: 110 (132, 148, 162, 178, 192)

Work in stockinette until piece measures 4½ (5, 5½, 6, 6½, 7) inches from end of ribbing.

On next row, k to 7 (7, 7, 7, 8, 10) sts before arm hole marker, BO 14 (14, 14, 14, 16, 20) sts, k to 7 (7, 7, 7, 8, 10) sts before arm hole marker, BO 14 (14, 14, 14, 16, 20) sts. Front and back are now separated.

Total front stitches: 108 (130, 144, 158, 172, 180)
Total back stitches: 96 (118, 134, 148, 162, 172)

Bodice Front:
Armhole shaping:
Working in stockinette, at the beginning of the next two rows, BO 4 sts.
On following rs rows, k1, ssk, k to last 3 sts, k2tog, k1.

Repeat this decrease each rs row 4 (5, 7, 9, 10, 12) more times, for a total of 5 (6, 8, 10, 11, 13) decreases. 18 (20, 24, 28, 30, 34) sts decreased.
Total stitches: 90 (110, 120, 130, 142, 146)

At the same time, when piece measures 6 (6½, 7, 7½, 8, 8½) inches from ribbing, work in pattern as set to center 30 (38, 40, 44, 48, 50) sts, attach new ball of yarn, BO 30 (38, 40, 44, 48, 50) sts, work in pattern as set to end.

This establishes the neckline.

Continue to work decreases if not completed by neckline BO. Working both straps at same time in stockinette, p across first strap, join a new ball of yarn on the second strap, BO 4 sts, p to end.

Next row, k across first strap on needles, BO 4 sts at beg of next strap, k to end.
Purl 1 row.
Next row, on first strap, k to last 3 sts, k2tog, k1.
On second strap, k1, ssk, k to end.

Repeat this decrease each rs row 5 (6, 7, 8, 9, 10) more times, for a total of 6 (7, 8, 9, 10, 11) decreases.

Then work the decrease row every 4th row 4 (5, 6, 7, 8, 9) times.

14 (16, 18, 20, 22, 24) sts decreased each strap.
Total stitches each strap: 16 (20, 22, 23, 25, 24)

Work in stockinette until straps measure 6½ (7, 7½, 8, 8½, 9) inches from armhole BO. Place remaining stitches on a holder.

Bodice Back:
Follow the armhole shaping instructions from the bodice front.
Total stitches: 78 (98, 110, 120, 132, 138)

When piece measures 6 (6½, 7, 7½, 8, 8½) inches from ribbing, work in pattern as set to center 26 (34, 38, 40, 44, 46) sts, join new ball of yarn, BO center 26 (34, 38, 40, 44, 46) sts, work in pattern as set to end.

Working both straps at same time in stockinette, p across first strap, on second strap BO 4 sts, p to end.
Next row, k across first strap on needles, BO 4 sts at beg of next strap, k to end.
Purl 1 row.
On following rs rows: On first strap k to last 3 sts, k2tog, k1. On second strap k1, ssk, k to end.

Repeat this decrease each rs row 5 (7, 9, 12, 14, 19) more times, for a total of 6 (8, 10, 13, 15, 20) decreases.
10 (12, 14, 17, 19, 22) sts decreased per strap.
16 (20, 22, 23, 25, 28) sts per strap.

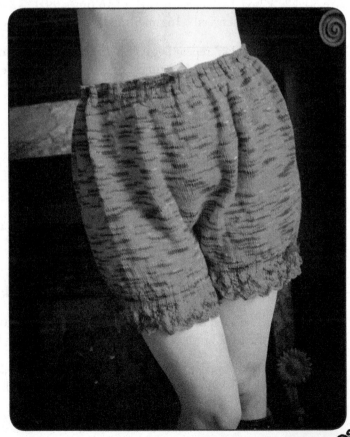

Work flat until straps measure 6½ (7, 7½, 8, 8½, 9) inches from armhole BO. Attach to front strap held stitches with a 3-needle BO.

Sleeve Ruffle (Make 2):
CO 49 (49, 58, 58, 67, 67) sts using size 7 needles.
K2, p to 2 sts before end, k2.

Next row, k2, work Lace Chart, end k2.

Continue in pattern, maintaining two stitch garter border, until piece measures 2 inches from cast on.

Switch to size 2 needles, work in 1x1 rib for five rows.
BO.

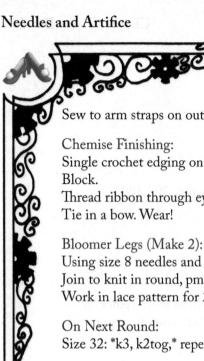

Sew to arm straps on outside, centering ruffle on either side of 3-needle BO seam.

Chemise Finishing:
Single crochet edging on inner neck and outer arm holes except where frill is.
Block.
Thread ribbon through eyelets in ribbing, centering in front.
Tie in a bow. Wear!

Bloomer Legs (Make 2):
Using size 8 needles and 24" cables, CO 180 (198, 216, 234, 252, 270) sts.
Join to knit in round, pm, k 1 row.
Work in lace pattern for 2½ (2½, 3, 3, 3½, 3½) inches.

On Next Round:
Size 32: *k3, k2tog,* repeat between * around.

Size 38: *k3, k2tog,* repeat between * 38 times total until 8 sts from end, k to end.

Size 42: k2, *k2tog, k4,* repeat between * 8 times total, *k2tog, k3,* repeat between * 23 times total, *k2tog, k4,* repeat between * 8 times total until 3 sts from end, k2tog, k1.

Size 46: k2, *k2tog, k4,* repeat between * 12 times total, *k2tog, k3,* repeat between * 17 times total, *k2tog, k4,* repeat between * 12 times total, until 3 sts from end, k2tog, k1.

Size 50: k2, *k2tog, k4,* repeat between * 16 times total, *k2tog, k3,* repeat between * 11 times total, *k2tog, k4,* repeat between * 16 times total, until 3 sts from end, k2tog, k1.

Size 54: k2, *k2tog, k4,* repeat between * 20 times total, *k2tog, k3,* repeat between * 5 times total, *k2tog, k4,* repeat between * 20 times total, until 3 sts from end, k2tog, k1.

36 (38, 40, 42, 44, 46) sts decreased.
Total stitches: 144 (160, 176, 192, 208, 224)

Switch to size 2 needles and work in 2x2 rib for ½".
On next row, work as follows: *k2, yo, p2tog, k2, p2,* repeat between * to end marker.
Work in 2x2 rib until rib measures 1".
Switch to size 5 needles.

Size 32: k2, *m1, k5,* repeat between * 12 times total, *m1, k4,* repeat between * 5 times total, *m1, k5,* repeat between * 12 times total, until 2 sts from end m1, k2.

Size 38: k2, *m1, k5,* repeat between * 7 times total, *m1, k6,* repeat between * 15 times total, *m1, k5,* repeat between * 6 times total, until 3 sts from end m1, k3.

Size 42: k3, *m1, k7,* repeat between * 12 times total, *m1, k6,* repeat between * 5 times total, *m1, k7,* repeat between * 12 times total, until 3 sts from end m1, k3.

Size 46: k3, *m1, k7,* repeat between * 7 times total, *m1, k6,* repeat between * 12 times total, *m1, k7,* repeat between * 7 times total, until 3 sts from end m1, k3.

Size 50: k4, *m1, k9,* repeat between * 4 times total, *m1, k16,* repeat between * 5 times total, *m1, k4,* repeat between * 12 times total, until 4 sts from end m1, k4.

Size 54: k4, *m1, k9,* repeat between * 3 times total, *m1, k10,* repeat between * 17 times total, *m1, k9,* repeat between * 2 times total, until 5 sts from end m1, k5.

Total stitches: 174 (189, 203, 217, 233, 247)

Work in stockinette until work measures 2½ (2¾, 3, 3¼, 3½, 3¾) inches from ribbing.

If working legs separately, put this leg aside, and work second leg to this point.

On each leg, slip the 42 (45, 51, 55, 57, 63) sts just worked to a holder. On first leg, k to end.
New total stitches per leg: 132 (144, 152, 162, 176, 184)

On next round, using 32" size 5 needles, place marker at crotch join (this is your new starting marker) and knit across second leg with working yarn from first leg, joining legs together with the held sts on both legs facing. These will become the crotch later.

Total stitches: 264 (288, 304, 324, 352, 368)

Place rear gusset markers: On next row, k93 (102, 107, 114, 123, 128) sts, pm, *k26 (28, 30, 32, 35, 37) sts, pm,* repeat between * twice more for a total of 3 repeats, k to end.

On next row, begin working gusset increases as follows:

Round 1: *k to first marker, m1, sm, k to second marker, sm, m1* twice, k to end. 4 sts increased.

Round 2: knit.
Round 3: knit.
Work these three rows 3 (7, 11, 13, 14, 17) more times for 4 (8, 12, 14, 15, 18) times total.
Total stitches: 276 (320, 348, 376, 408, 436)

Work in stockinette until piece measures 12 (13, 14, 15, 16, 17) inches from ribbing.

On next row, decrease for waist:
Size 32: k3, *k2tog, k6,* repeat between * 12 times total, *k2tog, k5,* repeat between * 11 times total, *k2tog, k6,* repeat between * 12 times total, until 4 sts from end, k2tog, k2.

Size 38: *k8, k2tog,* repeat between * 32 times total.

Size 42: k5, *k2tog, k11,* repeat between * 6 times total, *k2tog, k10,* repeat between * 15 times total, *k2tog, k11,* repeat between * 6 times total, until 7 sts from end, k2tog, k5.

Size 46: k7, *k2tog, k14,* repeat between * 8 times total, *k2tog, k13,* repeat between * 7 times total, *k2tog, k14,* repeat between * 8 times total, until 8 sts from end, k2tog, k6.

Size 50: *k15, k2tog,* repeat between * 24 times total.

Size 54: *k10, k2tog,* repeat between * 36 times total, end k4.

Total stitches: 240 (288, 320, 352, 384, 400)

Switch to size 2 needles and work in 2x2 rib for ¾".

On next row, work as follows: *k2, yo, p2tog, k2, p2,* repeat between * to end of round.

Continue in 2x2 rib until rib measures 1½".

Bind off with your preferred stretchy method.

FINISHING:
Using the kitchener stitch, graft together held stitches in crotch of bloomers, being sure to close up all holes. Block. Weave ribbon through eyelets on leg ribbing, centering on the outside thigh. Weave ribbon through eyelets in waist, centering in middle of waist.

Chart

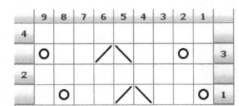

	9	8	7	6	5	4	3	2	1	
4										
	O			/\				O		3
2										
		O		\/					O	1

Legend:

yo
⊙ RS: Yarn Over
WS: Yarn Over

knit
☐ RS: knit stitch
WS: purl stitch

ssk
◺ RS: Slip one stitch as if to knit, Slip another stitch as if to knit. Insert left-hand needle into front of these 2 stitches and knit them together
WS: Purl two stitches together in back loops, inserting needle from the left, behind and into the backs of the 2nd & 1st stitches in that order

k2tog
◹ RS: Knit two stitches together as one stitch
WS: Purl 2 stitches together

The Indulgence Bed Jacket
By: Amanda Williams

DESCRIPTION:
This is a bed jacket with lots of ease. It is knit flat, top down to create a round yoke with short row shaping at the back neck, with the lace body falling in a heavily gathered style. It is seamless and has billowing sleeves with fitted cuffs. It closes with a button at the neck.

SPECIAL TECHNIQUES:
Backwards Loop Cast On

FINISHED DIMENSIONS:
Chest: 70 (75, 80)"
Length: 19"

TO FIT BODY MEASUREMENTS:
We have included 3 different sizes here. Because of the amount of ease in the garment, we expect that almost everyone will make the middle size (finished garment size of 75 inches). The other sizes are included to demonstrate how sizing adjustments can be made if you do wish to make a smaller or larger size.

A lady always makes time for a little luxury in life: decadent lace, rich colors, sensual textures. When it's high time for some lounging about, leave those boxy old things in the armoire! Surround your lovely self in this dreamy, blissful cloud of knitting, and even a quiet night at home can be an opulent escape.

YARN AND YARDAGE:

Kidsilk Lace by Hedgehog Fibers,
www.hedgehogfibres.com
70% kid mohair, 30% silk; 500yds (457m)
per 50g; lace weight
Color: Merlot, 3 (3, 3) skeins

Silk/Merino Singles by Hedgehog Fibers,
www.hedgehogfibres.com
50% silk, 50% Merino; 250yds (230m)
per 100g; worsted weight
Color: Merlot, 1 (1, 1) skein

Yarn special features for substitution: The
yoke uses a smooth bulky yarn with quite
a lot of shine to contrast with the fuzzy
laceweight chosen for the body to have
loft and warmth.

GAUGE:

Knitted and blocked gauge:
Contrast yarn in stockinette: 16 sts x 22
rows = 4"/10cm
Main yarn in pattern: one repeat = 2¾"
wide x 3¼" tall

NEEDLES AND NOTIONS:

16" size 8 US/5mm circular needle
16" size 6 US/4mm circular needle
40" size 4 US/3.5mm circular needle
Stitch markers
Tapestry needle
1 button (1" button used, but any large size button will work).

PATTERN NOTES :

This garment is knit top down starting with the bulky weight silk. At the body of the garment you
switch to the laceweight with a k1, yo, k1, yo, k1 in each stitch to increase the stitch count.

The entire garment is worked flat at once without side seams.

Pattern

Collar
The collar is knit as one piece from left side around the back to the right side.
Using size 8 needles and contrast yarn, cast on 213 stitches loosely.
Begin knitting flat.
Knit 6 rows in garter, ending with a right side row.

K3tog across all stitches. 71 stitches remain.
Change to size 6 needles.

K1, p1 to end ending with a k1.
Change back to size 8 needles.

Short row shaping for back neck center:
With rs facing, k1, p1, knit 51.
Wrap and turn, purl 35.
Wrap and turn, knit 37.
Wrap and turn, purl 39.
Wrap and turn, knit 41.
Wrap and turn, purl 43.
Wrap and turn, knit to 2 stitches before the end, p1, k1.

Yoke:
Set up row (ws): *k1, p1,* rep between * once more, k1 *pm, p10,* rep between * 5 more times, pm, k2, *p1, k1,* rep between * once more.

Row 1: * k1, p1,* rep between * once more, knit to marker, m1r, slip marker, rep 3 more times, *k to marker, slip marker, m1l,* rep between * 2 more times, k to 4 stitches before end, *p1, k1,* rep between * once more.

Row 2: purl back.

Row 3: * k1, p1,* rep between * once more, knit to marker, m1r, slip marker, *k to marker, m1, slip marker,* rep between * once more, *k to marker, slip marker, m1l,* rep between * 3 more times, k to 4 stitches before end, *p1, k1,* rep between * once more.

Row 4: purl back.

Repeat Rows one through four 4 (5, 4) times, then work to Row 2 (0, 2). There will be 134 (141, 134) stitches on the needles.
Break yarn.

Body:
With rs facing and using size 4 needles to knit off of the larger needles, join in main yarn. In this set up row you will establish the stitch count for the lace section.

For Small and Large sizes: while keeping the stitch on the left needle k1, yo, k1, then slip that stitch off and yo. Repeat 66 more times.
In the next stitch, k1, yo, k1, yo, k1.
In the next stitch, k1, yo, k1, then slip that stitch off and yo. Repeat 66 more times to the end of the row.
You should have 537 stitches on your needle.

For Medium size: while keeping the stitch on the left needle, k1, yo, k1, then slip that stitch off and yo. Repeat 69 more times.
In the next stitch, k1, yo, k1, yo, k1.
In the next stitch, k1, yo, k1, then slip that stitch off and yo. Repeat 70 more times to the end of the row.
You should have 565 stitches on your needle.
Purl back.

Begin Chart A on rs.

Work rows 1-24 once, then work rows 1-9 once.

On the next wrong side row (Row 10 of the lace pattern), work 6 repeats of the lace pattern, then slip 98 (112, 98) stitches to a holder (7 [8, 7] repeats of the lace pattern). Using backwards loop method, CO 14 (28, 42) stitches. Work across 12 more repeats of the lace pattern, then then slip 98 (112, 98) stitches to a holder (7 [8, 7] repeats of the lace pattern). Using backwards loop method, CO 14 (28, 42) stitches. Work across the remaining 6 lace repeats.

Continue working body of garment rows 11-24 of the lace pattern, then work through rows 1-24 two more times.

Work the 2 rows of Chart B for the border pattern across all stitches. Repeat Chart B 4 more times (5 times total), then work 6 rows of garter stitch and bind off loosely.

Sleeves:
Put held stitches onto size 4 needles. Pick up 14 (28, 42) stitches across the cast on underarm stitches and begin to work in the round. Beginning on row 10 of the lace pattern, continue through row 24. Then work rows 1-24 across all stitches 4 times. Break yarn.

Using size 6 needles and the contrast yarn, k4tog (k5tog, k5tog) around. Work in 1x1 ribbing for 4 inches. Bind off loosely.

Repeat for other arm.

CHART NOTES:
Chart A has a Central Double Decrease at the beginning of Round/Row 23. This stitch needs to borrow the last stitch of the previous repeat for that decrease. This allows the chart to remain lined up as in the rest of the pattern. For the sleeves you will need to borrow a stitch from the previous round. If you use stitch markers to delineate the repeats, you will need to adjust them on Row 23 to accommodate the borrowed stitch.

FINISHING:

Sew a button at the neckband with a loop of single crochet at the opposite side in contrast yarn to secure.

Charts

Chart A

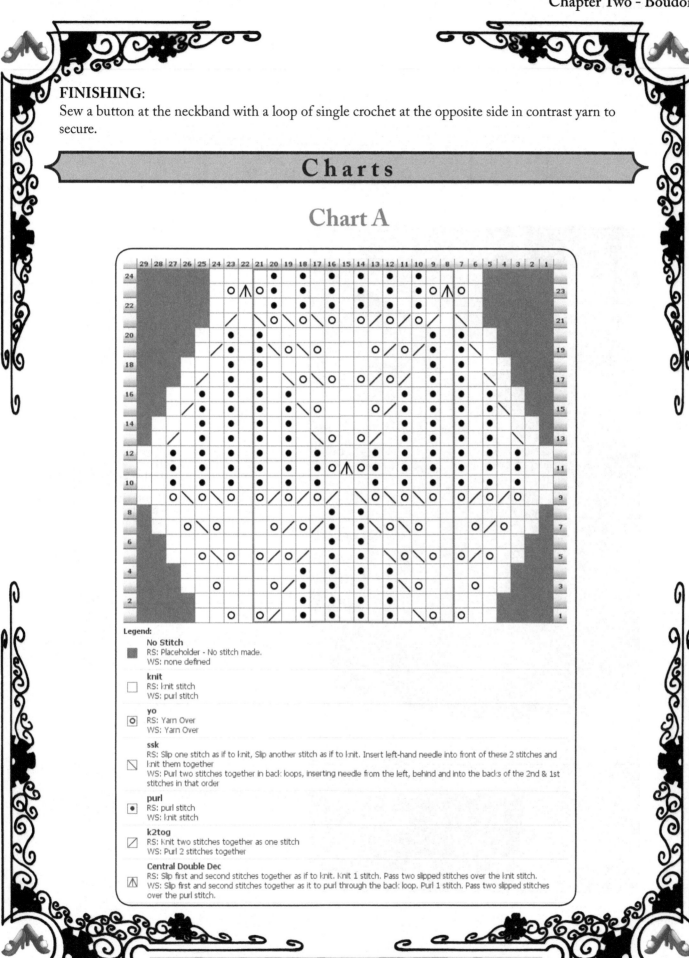

Legend:

No Stitch
RS: Placeholder - No stitch made.
WS: none defined

knit
RS: knit stitch
WS: purl stitch

yo
RS: Yarn Over
WS: Yarn Over

ssk
RS: Slip one stitch as if to knit, Slip another stitch as if to knit. Insert left-hand needle into front of these 2 stitches and knit them together
WS: Purl two stitches together in back loops, inserting needle from the left, behind and into the backs of the 2nd & 1st stitches in that order

purl
RS: purl stitch
WS: knit stitch

k2tog
RS: Knit two stitches together as one stitch
WS: Purl 2 stitches together

Central Double Dec
RS: Slip first and second stitches together as if to knit. Knit 1 stitch. Pass two slipped stitches over the knit stitch.
WS: Slip first and second stitches together as it to purl through the back loop. Purl 1 stitch. Pass two slipped stitches over the purl stitch.

Chart B

	19	18	17	16	15	14	13	12	11	10	9	8	7	6	5	4	3	2	1	
2																				
					O		O	/	/		\	\	O		O					1

Legend:

☐ **knit**
RS: knit stitch
WS: purl stitch

◉ **yo**
RS: Yarn Over
WS: Yarn Over

◩ **ssk**
RS: Slip one stitch as if to knit, Slip another stitch as if to knit. Insert left-hand needle into front of these 2 stitches and knit them together
WS: Purl two stitches together in back loops, inserting needle from the left, behind and into the backs of the 2nd & 1st stitches in that order

◪ **k2tog**
RS: Knit two stitches together as one stitch
WS: Purl 2 stitches together

The Hush Chemise

By: Amanda Williams

DESCRIPTION:

This top down chemise is designed to be worn under a corset but can be worn as a flirty summer top as well. Use the most luxurious, soft yarn you can find. Cashmere, silk, or merino are excellent choices. For a gauzy layered look, choose a cobweb type lace weight yarn. For more of a t-shirt style, you can choose something closer to fingering weight. As long as your fabric gets you the stated gauge and still has a nice drape to it, you'll have a lovely garment.

FINISHED DIMENSIONS:

Bust: 33¾ (37, 40½, 44¼, 48, 49¼, 53¾, 57¼)"
Length: Length is adjustable to suit your body and your tastes. As written it ends at the high hip.

Imagine tucking away a precious skein of cashmere, anticipating its softness between your hands as you knit this decadent lace. You deserve a delicious little secret... And though a lady should never reveal her secrets, you might let the merest hint peek over your corset. No matter how much of it you chose to show, you'll want this to be the closest thing to your skin.

TO FIT BODY MEASUREMENTS:
Bust: 32 (36, 39, 42, 46, 49, 52, 55)"

EASE:
Positive Ease. This garment fits closely at the bust, then falls straight down to the hips, giving it a generous waistline. Chose the size closest to your bust measurement. Consider changing needle sizes to change gauge for a closer fit if between sizes.

YARN AND YARDAGE:
50/50 Silk Merino by Dye for Yarn,
www.dyeforyarn.de
50% Merino, 50% silk; 765yds (700m) per 100g; lace weight
Color: Poisonous Honey, 1 (2, 2, 2, 2, 2, 3, 3) skeins

GAUGE:
Ball band gauge of chosen yarn: 33-40 sts = 4"
Knitted and blocked gauge:
In stockinette:
Large needle (US 4): 26 sts x 32 rows = 4"/10cm
Small needle (US 3): 28 sts x 44 rows = 4"/10cm
In pattern on Small needle (US 3): 1 repeat = 3½" wide x 1½" tall

NEEDLES AND NOTIONS:
32" size 3 US/3.25mm circular needle
32" size 4 US/3.5mm circular needle
Stitch markers

PATTERN NOTES:
The sizing for this garment is tied to the number of lace repeats you will have at the bottom. If you find yourself between sizes, consider changing needle size to adjust gauge for a more precise fit.

Pattern

Yoke:
Cast on 276 (299, 322, 368, 391, 391, 437, 460) stitches with smaller needle.
Place maker and begin to work in the round. This point will be your center front.

Work 4 rounds in garter stitch, starting with a knit round.
Work Row 1 of the Lace Chart 12 (13, 14, 16, 17, 17, 19, 20) times around.
Continue working the 12 rows of the Lace Chart pattern twice.
Work 4 rows in garter stitch.
Switch to larger needle.

In the next stitch, k1, yo, k1, yo, k1 then slip the stitch off the needle, then knit 18 (20, 22, 26, 28, 26, 31, 33) stitches. Repeat once more. This is the first half of the front.

Bind off 60 (64, 67, 75, 78, 82, 88, 93) stitches. This is the first sleeve.

Knit across 4 (3, 9, 4, 10, 5, 5, 2) stitches, then *m1, knit 3 (3, 3, 4, 4, 3, 4, 4),* repeat between * 23 (26, 25, 25, 24, 34, 30, 33) more times for a total of 24 (27, 26, 26, 25, 35, 31, 34) repeats. M1, then knit 5 (4, 10, 4, 11, 6, 6, 2) stitches. This is the back.

Bind off 60 (64, 67, 75, 78, 82, 88, 93) stitches. This is the second sleeve.

Knit across 18 (20, 22, 26, 28, 26, 31, 33) stitches.
In the next stitch, k1, yo, k1, yo, k1, then slip the stitch off the needle, knit 18 (20, 22, 25, 27, 27, 30, 32) stitches. This is the second half of the front.

Knit to end of front.
For back, join in new yarn, knit across back.

You will now begin working back and forth, keeping the Front and Back sections separate.

Turn and purl back.
Work both Front and Back in stockinette for 1", working flat.

Begin Armhole Shaping:
For both Back and Front sections, continue working in stockinette, increasing one stitch at each side edge every rs row 4 (4, 5, 5, 7, 9, 8, 9) times.
On the next rs row, knit across the Front section. Using the backwards loop method, cast on 2 stitches.
Repeat for the Back section, casting on 2 stitches.
Next ws row: purl across the Back section. Using the backwards loop method, cast on 2 stitches.
Repeat for the Front, casting on 2 stitches.

Next rs row: knit across the front. Using backwards loop method, cast on 1 (2, 4, 1, 1, 2, 2, 3) stitches. With the same yarn, continue knitting across the back.
Using backwards loop method, cast on 1 (3, 4, 2, 1, 3, 2, 4) stitches.
Begin knitting across the front to work in the round again.

Knit in plain stockinette until work measures 11¾ (13, 13, 14¼, 15½, 16, 16¼, 16¼) inches from the armhole or 1¾" shorter than desired length.

For sizes 32 (36, 39, 42, 46): *m1, knit 20 (19, 20, 26, 28),* repeat between * 10 (12, 12, 10, 10) times, m1, k19 (12, 23, 28, 31). Total stitches: 230 (253, 276, 299, 322)

For size 49: m1, then knit around. Total stitches: 322

For size 52: *k2tog, k85* 3 times, k2tog, k86. Total stitches: 345

For size 55: *k2tog, k91* 4 times. Total stitches: 368

Beginning at center front marker, work rows 1-12 of the lace pattern 10 (11, 12, 13, 14, 14, 15, 16) times around.

Work 4 rows in garter stitch.

Bind off loosely.

Chart

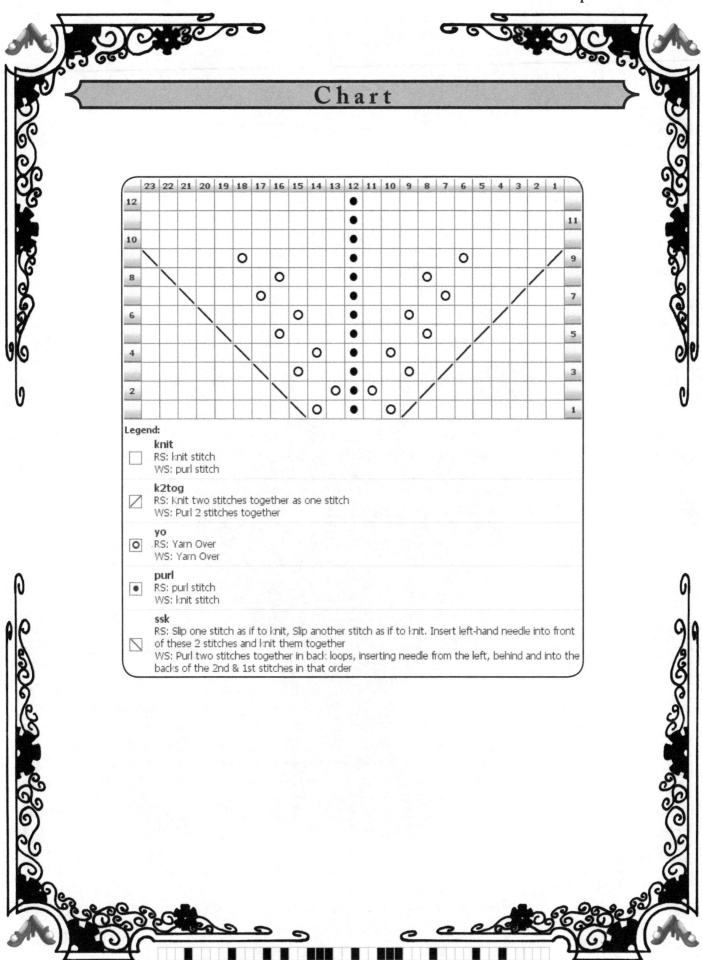

Legend:

knit
RS: knit stitch
WS: purl stitch

k2tog
RS: Knit two stitches together as one stitch
WS: Purl 2 stitches together

yo
RS: Yarn Over
WS: Yarn Over

purl
RS: purl stitch
WS: knit stitch

ssk
RS: Slip one stitch as if to knit, Slip another stitch as if to knit. Insert left-hand needle into front of these 2 stitches and knit them together
WS: Purl two stitches together in back loops, inserting needle from the left, behind and into the backs of the 2nd & 1st stitches in that order

Chapter Three

In which a most extraordinary airship conveys the Ladies

Coraline Hackworth had been pondering her mechanical globe, deciding where to fly next, when her brooch sounded. She leaped backwards from the globe and with a fierce battle cry kicked it off its stand. It was at that point that she realized the sound was coming from her own lapel. Well. The globe certainly knew who was in charge, now. With a slightly sheepish smile she moved to her desk and waved off the guards peering into her office. While she jotted down and deciphered the message from the brooch, two Hackworth engineers quietly entered the office and set to work repairing the globe. By the time she had the full message, the globe was completely restored and the engineers were gone. She hardly noticed, as her travel plans had just crystallized. She swept out of her office and began issuing commands to her assistant. It was time to get dear Lilith Ascending ready for an emergency flight.

****

Miss Coraline Hackworth's airships carried the Ladies around the globe. Growing up, she split her time between the Hackworth airshipyard and the ballrooms of London's society families. From the airshipyard, she learned about the value of hard work, clear communication, and excellent design. From the ballrooms, she learned how to temper her commanding presence with formal manners (a bit). Her keen intellect was stimulated both by the technical intricacies of airship design and the push and pull of interpersonal relations. At the age of 18, she began assuming management duties at the airshipyard, and quashed all doubt by simultaneously improving productivity and working conditions. At the age of 20 she designed and launched a new airship line to meet the growing cargo transport needs of the nation. In a move previously unheard of, she was named president of Hackworth Airships International at age 26, with full approval of the Board of Directors. Within the company, she launched a campaign of global expansion and scientific advancement. She kept a hand in the design and research while adventuring around the globe to scope out new airship lines.

The Ladies (and gentleman) waiting in the foggy meadow outside of Shanghai didn't see the airship until it was nearly upon them. One moment they were alone, knitting in the chill air and reminiscing about the morning's hot tea, and the next moment the fog parted around the sharp polished prow of an unusually tall and narrow airship. It cut through the fog like a blade, causing delightful eddies and swirls in the mist. The airship settled to ground with a soft whoosh of bending grass. The spellbound silence was cut by Coraline's voice booming from the ship.

"Excellent landing, everyone! As smooth and pleasant as the finest silk yarn. We have a quick turnaround, so get ready to take off in 5!"

The crew extended the gangplank in a flash. Coraline strode down towards the Ladies, her proud smile turning to something softer as she drew close.

"Alyssa! Anna! Kitty! It's good to see you! We'll have you in London in no time—YOU!" Her eyes snapped to Kristoff and she lunged towards him, pushing Caldonia protectively behind her. "What are you doing here? Your pathetic ransom attempt failed, did you think you could strike at me through my friends?"

Kristoff paled and took a small step backwards as her accusing finger nearly poked him in the nose. This close, her voice managed to get even louder. "If you bother my friends, you're making this personal. If you make this personal, I won't hold back!" Anna sighed inwardly, pushed Kristoff backwards and stepped directly in front of Coraline. This sudden movement caused Coraline to stop yelling for a short moment, though her finger remained pointed at Kristoff. The other Ladies noticed that they were now surrounded by a grim-faced and well-armed airship crew.

"Kristoff Von Boltenstein, may I introduce Miss Coraline Hackworth?" Alyssa glanced briefly around them. "Excuse me, I mean Captain Coraline Hackworth."

Captain Coraline Hackworth's aggrieved response to Kristoff was actually quite appropriate after her most recent misadventure. She had traveled to a Scientific Exposition to view the latest advances and discuss theories with the great scientific minds of the age. While there, she became intrigued by a clockwork mechanism that could sense and respond to the world around it. She arranged a meeting with the reclusive inventor, only to find herself kidnapped at the meeting place. Coraline was unperturbed; as the only child of a very rich and powerful family, she had been kidnapped countless times and was fully capable of extricating herself. The kidnappers were taking her to the inventor, so she chose to remain on their ship, and suffered no worse than the temporary separation from her possessions. She even managed to covertly use the onboard communications, and discovered that her companion Peter Thistleby was following at a discreet distance in her airship, Lilith Ascending. After landing somewhere north of London, she was taken to the inventor and began to query him about her topics of interest: the clockwork mechanism, the inventor himself, and the security systems of her room of confinement. Klaus Von Boltenstein did not like her commanding tone or pointed questions, and several times threatened to dispose of her. However, he couldn't resist a fresh audience, and ended up telling her everything she wanted to know, and a good number of things she had no interest in. He finally wound down and sent her to her room, after which she quickly made her escape. A few months had passed, and she had thought the matter closed and behind her until she landed her airship near Shanghai and was surprised to discover her captor standing with a group of the Ladies.

At Alyssa's introduction, Coraline realized that the gentleman before her, whom Anna was defending, was not the same man. "A twin brother! How astounding! You must be the one that Klaus hates so!" For she had accidentally triggered an extended monologue about revenge against the family while interrogating Klaus.

"I'm afraid the feeling is becoming mutual," Kristoff muttered darkly.

"Stand down, everyone!" Coraline shouted. "A case of mistaken identity! I am perfectly secure, and my new acquaintance Kristoff here is to be treated with the utmost respect." Coraline caught the eye of her first mate. "Good show Perkins! I'm quite pleased with your precision and stealth!" The first mate smiled briefly, nodded, then with a sharp hand gesture she lead the crew back onto the airship.

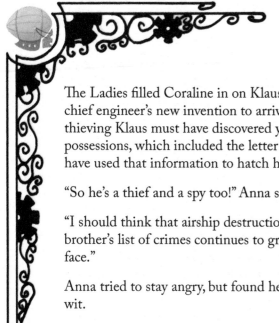

The Ladies filled Coraline in on Klaus' plot. "I know just where the estate is, and we will use my chief engineer's new invention to arrive unseen." Coraline drew in a sharp breath. "Oh no! That thieving Klaus must have discovered your location from me! When I was kidnapped, he took all my possessions, which included the letter from you, Anna, telling of your rescue of Kristoff. He must have used that information to hatch his replacement plan and send his air pirates after you!"

"So he's a thief and a spy too!" Anna snarled.

"I should think that airship destruction was sufficient to condemn him," Kristoff said gravely, "but my brother's list of crimes continues to grow. I think you shall have to kick his arse *and* punch him in the face."

Anna tried to stay angry, but found herself fighting back a smile. Kristoff was really becoming quite a wit.

"For all his crimes, we must teach him that he crossed the wrong group of Ladies!" Coraline announced, then paused. "And gentleman of course." She added a slight bow to Kristoff.

"Now you must come aboard my dear Lilith Ascending - no time to waste!" Coraline strode away, shouting orders before she was halfway up the gangplank. While the ladies tucked away their knitting and began drifting onto the peculiar ship, Kristoff leaned close to Anna.

"Is she always so...forceful?" Kristoff was still a little pale. He hadn't been shouted at like that since... Well, technically, the previous morning. Anna slipped her hand into his and squeezed warmly. "I thought you'd be used to women shouting at you by now," she replied, a mischievous twinkle in her eye. "When she's on her ship, she's Captain Coraline Hackworth. Every word she says is a command. When she's meeting with the Ladies, she's just Cora."

"Then it's only every other word!" Caldonia chimed in. The Ladies all laughed.

"Cora does try to tell us what to do..." Alyssa began.

"Have you heard of the expression 'trying to herd cats'?" Caldonia was grinning now. "Replace cats with tigers and you get the idea."

"Yes, her roar is definitely worse than her bite!" Anna finished, then frowned. "Granted, she hasn't actually bitten any of us. She might bite very hard..." In the next moment everyone clearly heard Coraline shouting orders on the ship. The Ladies smiled fondly and Kristoff relaxed. They boarded, and entered the airship bridge.

"To the skies! We're going to Montana!" At Coraline's words, the crew sprang into action, raising the gangplank, pulling ropes, stoking the engines and otherwise scurrying about. Coraline settled back in her captain's chair and smiled with satisfaction. Anna sat down in a corner and started cleaning her rifle, trying not to be impressed with the airship.

"I'm sorry, why are we going to Montana? London is, I am fairly certain, almost entirely in the other direction." Kristoff was still slightly confused, and starting to get a bit annoyed.

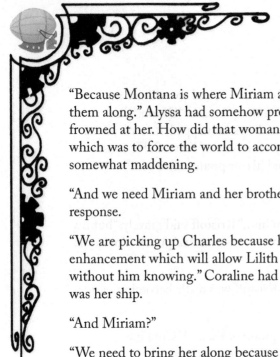

"Because Montana is where Miriam and her brother Charles are, darling, and we need to bring them along." Alyssa had somehow procured a cup of tea, which she was sipping demurely. Kristoff frowned at her. How did that woman always look so perfectly at home? It wasn't the way Anna did it, which was to force the world to accommodate her, regardless of consequences. Alyssa just...fit. It was somewhat maddening.

"And we need Miriam and her brother because..." Kristoff let the question hang in the air, awaiting a response.

"We are picking up Charles because he is my finest engineer, and he's been working on an enhancement which will allow Lilith Ascending to land almost on top of your brother's estate without him knowing." Coraline had also acquired a cup of tea. Well, at least that made sense. This was her ship.

"And Miriam?"

"We need to bring her along because if we don't, we'll never hear the end of it." This came from Anna. How in blazes had she managed to find a cup of tea?! She hadn't even left the corner where she'd been cleaning her rifle.

"Really? That's the reason? Because you'll never hear the end of it?"

All four ladies nodded, Caldonia while deeply inhaling the steam from her tea. Her tea? Kristoff sighed and ran his hands through his hair. "All right then. But then we'll go straight to London, correct? Gah!" A rather dashing goatee-wearing man had appeared right next to him without Kristoff noticing. The man raised an eyebrow and held out a small tray.

"Tea?"

Kristoff sighed, took the cup, and sat down.

"Ladies, meet Peter Thistleby." Coraline looked somewhat like a cat that had just stolen a large saucer of cream. "He stowed away in one of my best-hidden secret compartments. When I discovered him I found him much too interesting to throw overboard."

"Your charity to a wandering freelance mechanist was truly honorable." Peter seemed entertained by the captain's confidence in her ability to dispatch him.

"He's proven himself quite handy with engines and excellent under pressure. He's been traveling with me and assisting with...all manner of things." Was Coraline blushing? Alyssa and Caldonia exchanged a knowing look. Anna remained oblivious, re-assembling her gun with a practiced hand.

"Well he certainly manages the tea quite well." Kristoff was impressed but still a little put out.

"The tea? Oh yes...he does keep the tea flowing. Indeed." Coraline definitely had a pink tinge to her cheeks now. "It's time to check on the crew. Peter, please accompany me on my rounds."

"It would be my pleasure." Peter held out his arm and the two departed the bridge. They were barely around the corner when both Alyssa and Caldonia burst into laughter.

When she could breathe, Caldonia squeaked, "I've never seen Cora like that. He must be quite handy indeed!"

Kristoff pretended not to hear that last remark, and took another sip of his truly excellent tea.

***

"What exactly are you planning to do with so much chloroform?" Caldonia's voice held curiosity and possibly a hint of envy.

"It's part of my newest line of non-lethal weapons systems." Coraline's eyes sparkled with delight. "This particular batch is for use with the cannon nets. We load the weighted net into the cannon, pour a bottle down the barrel and then launch the whole thing towards whoever must be subdued. The Sleeper Net, as we're calling it currently, will also come in handy when it's necessary to contain some sort of living experiment gone wrong. Provided that the experiment needs to breathe."

The Ladies nodded sagely, having all experienced a person, thing, or group of such that would have been greatly improved by unconsciousness. Anna reflected that it would have been a handy thing indeed the previous morning, but spotted a flaw in the design.

"That's not very useful if you aren't carrying a cannon with you." Anna stroked her rifle possessively.

"You don't have to tell me that! We've been working on a ceramic cannonball that will shatter on impact and spread the chloroform. Once we have that figured out, it's only a matter of time until we can make smaller shots for shotguns and perhaps rifles." Coraline eyed Anna's gun, causing Anna to simultaneously grip it tighter and tilt it until the light caught the metalwork in an appealing gleam.

The other Ladies roamed around the interior of the ship again, looking for the next marvel. They had been touring the Lilith Ascending for an hour so far, and had only seen a fraction of the improvements. Kristoff had stayed in the bridge, rather grumpy at the extra travel time.

Coraline's personal ship was first in line to receive the new Hackworth inventions. Many of the inventions failed to live up to their potential; the evidence of small fires or explosions appeared on several of the walls. The inventions that did work were somewhat astonishing. The Ladies had already seen an amazing glowing globe in the captain's cabin that noted the ship's current location in the world with a roaming brass star. It managed this with magnets, somehow, though Coraline was very close-lipped about it. In the belly of the ship they had seen recoil-less cannons, able to shoot without knocking the ship sideways. Anna had made a mental note to request some to put in the Arcadia II. Would sixteen be enough, she wondered... On the main level, every interior surface was covered with a multitude of brass pipes, in all different sizes and a few different colors. The interior passageways had been comfortably wide, however the layers of pipes standing up from the walls made it necessary to move carefully. Next to the mundane pipes that transported steam, air or sounds, were pipes with a more unusual purpose. Thin pipes along the ceiling had small lead weights along them, which shifted constantly in a mesmerizing dance. Coraline explained that they managed the ballast of the airship, constantly adjusting for the crew's movements to keep the ship level.

"Look here." Coraline pointed to a pipe at waist height.

"It appears to have an eye painted on it. Possibly Egyptian in origin? It's quite lovely, really..." Alyssa leaned forward to inspect the pipe more closely.

"We call this one the Everseeing Eye! It has a clever collection of mirrors inside that allow me to view out the side of the ship from the bridge. The engineer that created it was quite taken with Egyptian tomb design. We're probably fortunate that it isn't cursed."

"I would find it quite...useful to be able to peek into a distant room unobserved..." Alyssa's voice trailed off as she smiled with delight. A light flush rose in her cheeks.

"And what is this one with the green hash marks on it?" Anna started to reach for a pipe near her knee.

"Don't touch that!" Coraline stepped back, away from Anna. "That experiment...didn't exactly work out. I'm afraid it's currently too dangerous to remove. Someday we'll figure out how to get it out of here safely." Anna raised an eyebrow and looked back at the pipe. Carnivorous grass, perhaps?

"Is that...a snake painted on this pipe?" Kitty was kneeling to look closely at a pipe near the floor. A crew member with a slightly goofy grin stood next to her, ready to help her stand. Each Lady was being escorted by several young men among the crew who were eager to assist their every move. They had been given orders to make sure the Ladies were taken care of, and they took their job extremely seriously. The poor fellow assigned to Anna looked rather crestfallen, as she had refused his every offer of assistance. Anna privately reflected that this happened every time she flew with Coraline, and wondered why no one ever seemed to learn.

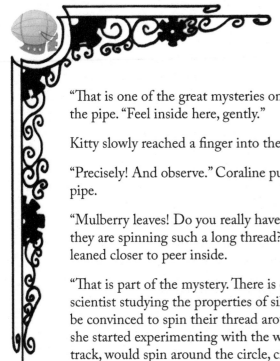

"That is one of the great mysteries on the ship." Coraline knelt next to Kitty and opened a hatch into the pipe. "Feel inside here, gently."

Kitty slowly reached a finger into the pipe. "It feels like a bundle of silk thread inside."

"Precisely! And observe." Coraline pulled a leaf from a box on the wall and gently placed it inside the pipe.

"Mulberry leaves! Do you really have silkworms in there?" Kitty looked confused. "And how is it that they are spinning such a long thread?" Anna knelt and peered into the pipe, fascinated. Even Alyssa leaned closer to peer inside.

"That is part of the mystery. There is only one worm, a jolly big one. I was chatting with a Hackworth scientist studying the properties of silk, and mentioned how lovely it would be if silkworms could be convinced to spin their thread around a spindle, instead of themselves. After that conversation she started experimenting with the worms, and somehow created one that, when placed in a circular track, would spin around the circle, creating an incredibly long thread. This pipe wraps all the way around the interior of the ship, and the worm traverses the whole length, spinning as it goes. I once told my father that I'd like a silk-wrapped airship for a birthday present. It was great fun to tell him that I had finally gotten my wish!"

"So what is the other part of the mystery?" Kitty asked.

Coraline's smile dropped away. "The greater mystery is how she did it. Shortly after discovering the circular path, the scientist began to believe that she could speak with the worms. Two months later, she stopped speaking English entirely, only speaking Worm and refusing to leave the lab. We still collect and save her notes, hoping that someday we will be able to translate whatever she's writing about."

"You mean she still works for you?" Alyssa was aghast.

Coraline nodded sadly. "She doesn't actually produce anything, other than scribbles, but it seemed cruel to make her leave her precious worms. So instead we removed the equipment and left her the worms and some basic furniture." The Ladies shared a shocked look.

"So your employee is now your prisoner." Kitty stood with much assistance and brushed off her skirt as if removing a rather disgusting stain.

Iron crept in to Coraline's voice. "Science is a harsh mistress. She destroys many who walk her paths. I have a responsibility to my employees, so I care for them as best I can. Her family agrees that it's the best solution."

"Are there other crackpots like her?" Anna's bravado was nearly perfect, with only a slight waver in her voice betraying her sympathy. She still attempted to spot the giant silkworm, hoping it would wriggle into view from somewhere down the pipe.

"Sadly, several. We have an entire division that manages the care of those who have...lost themselves in their work for us." Coraline drew a shaking breath and fell silent.

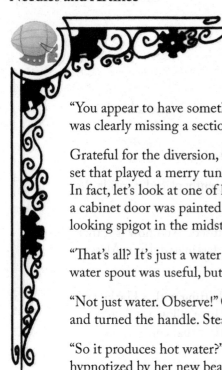

"You appear to have something missing here." Anna gestured at a blank area of the wall where a pipe was clearly missing a section. "Did the giant silkworm fancy a snack?"

Grateful for the diversion, Coraline cleared her throat. "Well, that used to be a lovely steam whistle set that played a merry tune on the hour, but Peter felt that the parts would be more useful elsewhere. In fact, let's look at one of his inventions now." Coraline lead the way to the end of the hall, where a cabinet door was painted with an elaborate Dahlia motif. She opened it to reveal a rather plain looking spigot in the midst of a china cupboard.

"That's all? It's just a water spout?" Anna bluntly stated what the Ladies were feeling. Certainly a water spout was useful, but she had one in her own airship and it was hardly worth a grand reveal.

"Not just water. Observe!" Coraline picked up a teapot, added a scoop of tea, held it under the tap, and turned the handle. Steaming water poured from the tap.

"So it produces hot water?" Kitty asked gently. She secretly wondered if Coraline had been hypnotized by her new beau.

"It's water that is always the perfect temperature for tea! Ready at all hours! And it never runs out! Peter devised a clever system that uses the waste heat from the boiler to provide perfectly heated water at all times. He hooked it into the ship's water system, then adjusted it for days until it met his exacting standards. Now my crew and I can have perfect tea any time we want! No waiting for the kettle to boil! In fact, try this." Coraline served tea out of the teapot to the Ladies.

"Mmm, this is fabulous tea. I wonder if a boiler would fit in my kitchen?" Alyssa tried to peer behind the cabinet.

"Could this system be used to create a shower compartment on an airship? And yes, Alyssa, I do bathe, so you needn't say whatever you are thinking." Anna bounced on her feet a little with excitement, while Alyssa politely closed her mouth, looking slightly put out.

Coraline grinned. "I'm sure Peter will be excited to expand the system. He always says that the best way to get something done is to build a machine to do it for you! He nearly swooned when I first showed him the Hackworth machine shop."

"Well, we all understand the joy of making something by hand." Alyssa stroked her sumptuous silk scarf. The ladies all took a moment to admire it.

The beauty of the scarf inspired Coraline. "I think it's time to retire to the bridge for some knitting and tea. We still have several hours before we'll reach Montana, and I can't imagine a more pleasant way to spend it."

Anna looked somewhat crestfallen at the mention of knitting, and the others turned to her in concern. "Whatever is the matter, dear?" Coraline asked, resting a hand on Anna's shoulder. Anna looked up at her sadly.

"Almost all of my yarn went down with the Arcadia," she lamented. "My knitting bag survived, but I'm done with all of my projects! Coraline, I have nothing to knit!" The Ladies all shuddered in sympathy. Coraline recoiled and shook her head sharply.

"My dearest Anna, that simply will not do! Come with me and avail yourself of my yarn room! We'll meet the rest of you back on the bridge!" With that, the two of them strode off down the hall, a decided spring back in Anna's step. A yarn room? Anna had confined her collection to a small closet on the Arcadia. Hackwork airships really did have their benefits.

The Helm's A-Lee Mitts
By: Valerie DiPietro

Romantic and ladylike? Or functional protection? If circumstances call for you to step in and pull the ropes like a deck hand, then by all means do so. But protect your hands and stay looking like the Lady Captain you are! And do have a cup of tea when you are done. No need to change your gloves; they will look lovely and appropriate at the table as well.

DESCRIPTION:
Fingerless elbow length gloves knit in the round. Worked in twisted rib with a traveling cable up the back of the hand, and left and right thumb gussets.

FINISHED DIMENSIONS:
12" long and 8" around top of palm

YARN AND YARDAGE:
Superwash Merino Wool Silk by Sunnyside Ellen, http://sunnysideellen.etsy.com
75% superwash merino, 25% silk; 440yds (400m) per 100g; fingering weight
Color: Airborne, 1 skein

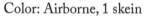

GAUGE:

Knitted and blocked gauge:
In stockinette in the round: 40 sts x 42 rows = 4"/10cm

NEEDLES AND NOTIONS:

One set size 2 US/2.75mm dpns or circular needle for working in the round
Stitch markers
2 stitch holders

PATTERN NOTES:

This pattern is easy to modify for a custom fit, as the cable repeat between the stitch markers remains unaffected by the decreases used to shape the glove.

Simply adjust the decreases (or adds increases) to get the best possible fit.

Pattern

CO 64 sts.

Join in the round, distribute evenly over 4 dpns, being careful not to twist stitches.

Work 1x1 twisted rib (work the knit sts tbl) for 1½ inches.

You will now place your first marker. This will be the beginning of your round.

Pm, k26, pm, work to end of round.

You will now start knitting the charts. All charts should be worked in the following manner, unless indicated otherwise: sm, work charted pattern row, sm, work to end.

Knit Chart A rows 1-19 once.

Begin working Chart B.

Work rows 1-24 of Chart B four times, ending the fourth repeat on Row 13. If you choose to modify length, end your last repeat of this section on Row 13.

At the same time decrease one stitch at the beginning and end of the stockinette portion of the row every 10 rows until you have 48 stitches.

Thumb Gusset, Right Glove:

Continue working Chart B starting at Row 14. At the same time work thumb gusset as follows:

Round 1: work pattern row, sm, m1, k1, m1, pm, work to end.
Round 2: work pattern row, sm, k3, sm, work to end.
Round 3: work pattern row, sm, m1, k3, m1, sm, work to end.

Continue working Rounds 2 and 3, adding 2 sts between gusset markers every odd row, until there are 15 sts worked between the markers. This should occur on pattern Row 23 of Chart B.
Next round: work last pattern row of Chart B, slip marker, place 15 gusset stitches on waste yarn or a holder, cast on 3 stitches, work remaining stitches.

Thumb Gusset, Left Glove:

Continue working Chart B starting at Row 14, at the same time work thumb gusset as follows:

Work until the last stitch of the stockinette portion (1 stitch before marker).
Round 1: pm, m1, k1, m1, sm, work pattern row, sm, work to gusset marker (new end of round).
Round 2: sm, k3, sm, work pattern row, sm, work to end.

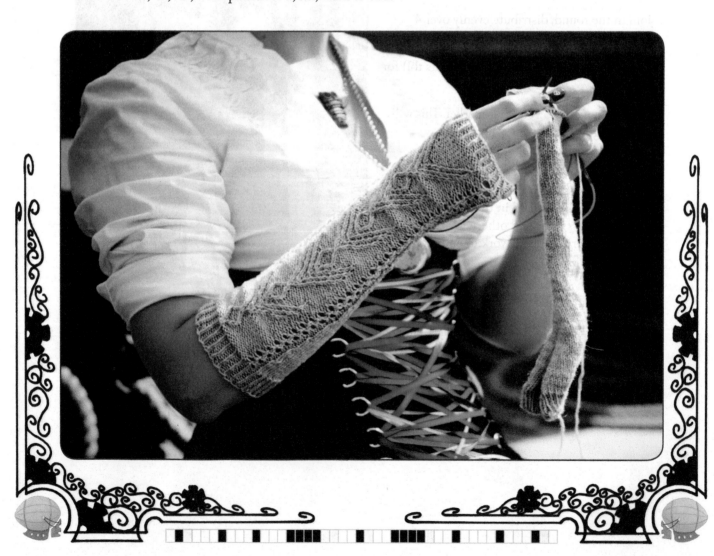

Round 3: sm, m1, k3, m1, sm, work pattern row, sm, work to end.

Continue working rows 2 and 3, adding 2 sts between gusset markers every odd row, until there are 15 sts worked between the markers. This should occur on pattern Row 23 of Chart B.

Next round: place 15 gusset stitches on waste yarn or a holder, cast on 3 stitches, work last pattern row of Chart B, remove marker, work remaining stitches.

Continue for both gloves:
Work Chart C once, continuing stockinette portion on palms.
Work 1½ inch 1x1 twisted rib across all sts.
Bind off loosely in pattern.

Thumb:
Using dpns, place held stitches on needle, pick up three stitches over gap. Work 5 rounds in stockinette. Work 1x1 twisted rib for 6 rounds. Bind off loosely.

Charts

Chart A

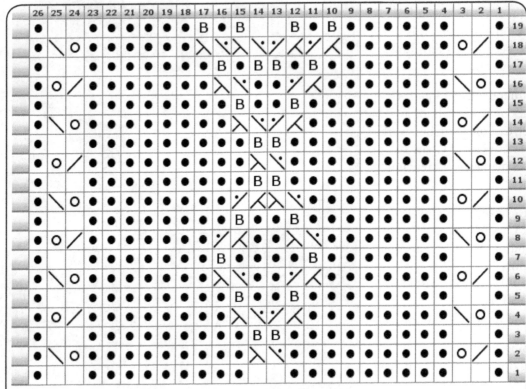

Legend:

⊙	**purl**	purl stitch
☐	**knit**	knit stitch
⧄	**k2tog**	Knit two stitches together as one stitch
⊙	**yo**	Yarn Over
⧅⊡	**Left Twist, purl bg**	sl1 to CN, hold in front. p1. k1 from CN
⧄	**ssk**	Slip one stitch as if to knit, Slip another stitch as if to knit. Insert left-hand needle into front of these 2 stitches and knit them together
B	**knit tbl**	Knit stitch through back loop
⧄⊡	**Right Twist, purl bg**	sl1 to CN, hold in back. k1, p1 from CN

Chart B

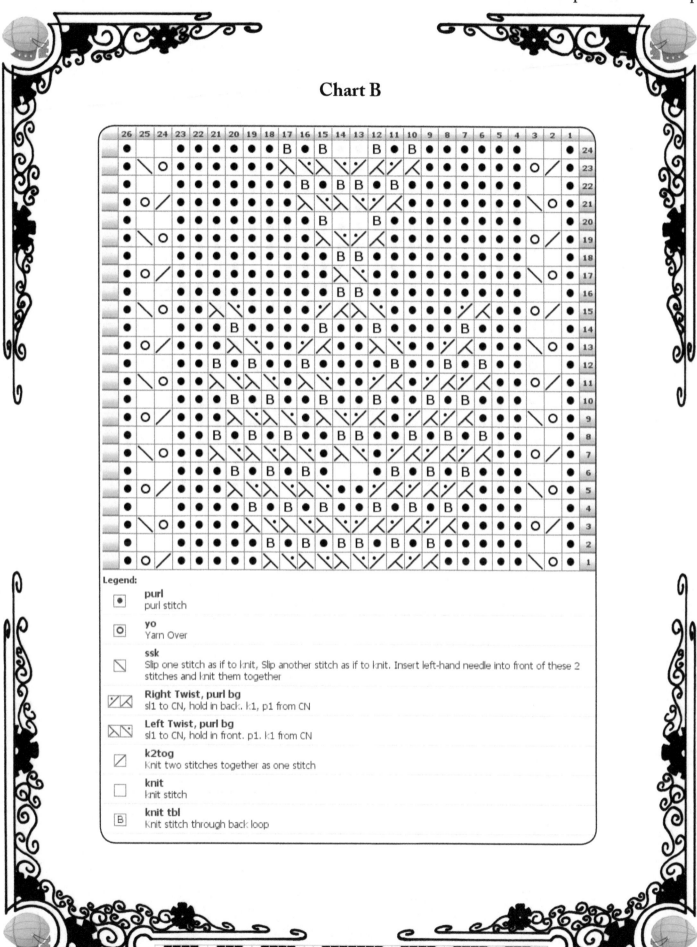

Legend:

●	**purl**	purl stitch
○	**yo**	Yarn Over
╲	**ssk**	Slip one stitch as if to knit, Slip another stitch as if to knit. Insert left-hand needle into front of these 2 stitches and knit them together
╱╲	**Right Twist, purl bg**	sl1 to CN, hold in back. k1, p1 from CN
╲╲	**Left Twist, purl bg**	sl1 to CN, hold in front. p1, k1 from CN
╱	**k2tog**	Knit two stitches together as one stitch
□	**knit**	knit stitch
B	**knit tbl**	Knit stitch through back loop

Chart C

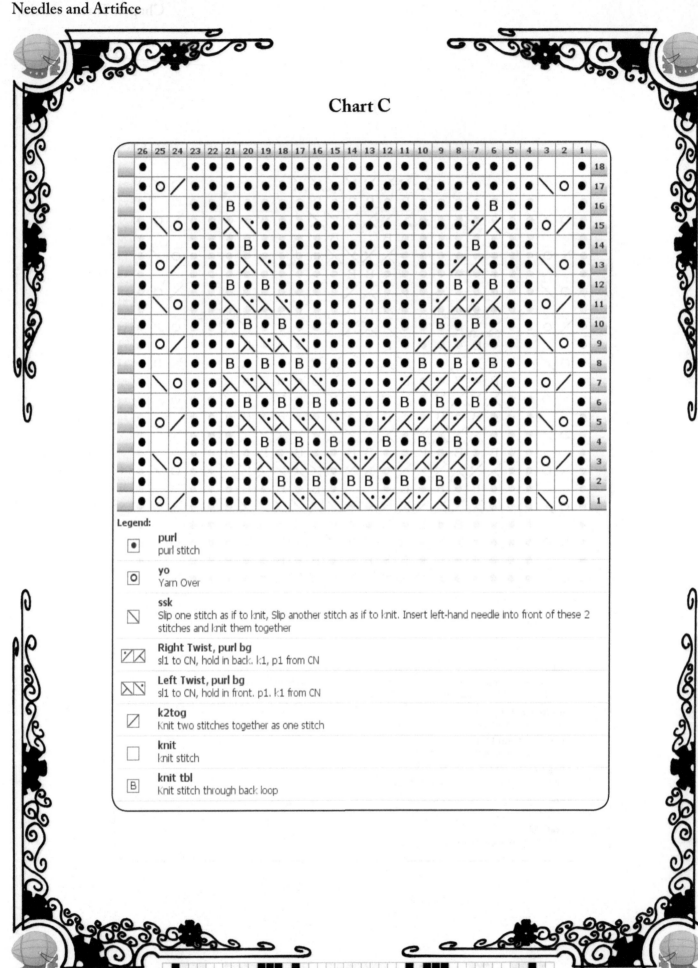

Legend:

⊡	**purl**	purl stitch
⊙	**yo**	Yarn Over
◺	**ssk**	Slip one stitch as if to knit, Slip another stitch as if to knit. Insert left-hand needle into front of these 2 stitches and knit them together
	Right Twist, purl bg	sl1 to CN, hold in back. k1, p1 from CN
	Left Twist, purl bg	sl1 to CN, hold in front. p1, k1 from CN
◿	**k2tog**	Knit two stitches together as one stitch
□	**knit**	knit stitch
B	**knit tbl**	Knit stitch through back loop

The Legacy Frock Coat

By: Sarra Loew

DESCRIPTION:
This close-fitting shrug is knit cuff to cuff, then stitches are picked up around the opening and worked with short rows to add the collar and body.

SPECIAL TECHNIQUES:
Crochet Cast On, Short Rows, Single Crochet.

FINISHED DIMENSIONS:
Cross back (shoulder to shoulder directly above the armpit): 14 (15, 16, 17, 17½, 18, 18, 18½, 18½)"

Upper arm: 9¾ (10½, 11, 12, 13½, 15½, 17, 18½, 19½)"

When Coraline took up the mantle of running the family business, she literally took up Grandpappy Hackworth's mantle; his frock coat fashioned in the 1820's to keep a gentleman warm, stylish and unencumbered while riding horseback was well suited to the demands of piloting an airship. Coraline redesigned it to express her style as a modern Victorian woman, while giving a loving nod to the grandfather she adored.

EASE:
No ease.

YARN AND YARDAGE:
Fidalgo by Woolgatherings,
http://www.woolgatheringsfibers.com
100% superwash merino; 118yds (108m) per 113g; bulky weight
Color A: Admiral, 6 (7, 7, 8, 9, 9, 10, 11, 12) skeins
Color B: Fog, 1 skein for all sizes

GAUGE:

Ball band gauge of chosen yarn:
In stockinette: 14 sts x 22 rows =
4"/10cm

Knitted and blocked gauge:
In stockinette in the round: 15 sts x 22
rows = 4"/10cm

NEEDLES AND NOTIONS:

One set size 10 US/6mm double
pointed needles (for working sleeves on
double points)
-OR-
Two 24" size 10 US/6mm circular
needles (for working sleeves on two
circulars)
-AND-
One 40" size 10 US/6mm circular
needle (required regardless of sleeve
method)
One size 10/J US/6mm crochet hook
Tapestry needle

PATTERN NOTES:

This pattern can be easily customized
to match your exact measurements.
Start by knitting a swatch in
stockinette in the round, then blocking
it. This step is especially important
if you wish to substitute a yarn that
contains silk or plant fibers, as those
yarns are known to stretch after
blocking. Once you have your blocked

swatch, note your gauge (stitches and rows). Enter your gauge in the following calculations:

Total bicep stitches: stitch gauge __ x Bicep measurement in inches __ +12 = __ stitches
Arm length: row gauge __ x Arm length measurement in inches __ = __ rows
Shoulder width: row gauge __ x (Cross back measurement in inches + 6 (XS-L) or 8 (XL-5X)) __ =
__ rows
Extra space has been provided in the pattern to allow you to enter your customized numbers
throughout.

The crochet cast on and knit bind off are used to make the two cuffs match as closely as possible. The
XS/S sizes do not have sleeve increases or decreases.

As written, the cuff will extend halfway over the hands. Try the sleeve on as you go for a custom fit.

Remember to use your gauge swatch to verify the blocked length by counting your rows. To add or remove length, change the number of rows worked after the increases.

Pattern

With MC, cast on 52 stitches using the crochet cast on.
Join to work in the round.
Work in 1x1 rib for 4 inches.

Cuff Decrease:

Round 1: k1, ssk, work in established pattern to 3 stitches from end of round, k2tog, k1.
Round 2: work in established pattern.

Repeat these two rows 5 more times. 40 stitches now remain.
Purl 1 round.

Sleeve:

XS (S): work in stockinette until piece measures 18½ (19, __) inches/102 (105, __) rows or desired length. This is the sleeve length to the armhole, the shoulder is included in the flat section.

Sleeve Increase:

M (L, 1X, 2X): work in stockinette for 10 (8, 4, 4, __) rows.

Increase row: k1, m1k, knit to end.

Repeat increase row every 32 (7, 4, 2, __) rows 1 (5, 9, 17, __) more times, working plain rows in stockinette. Total stitches: 42 (46, 50, 58, __)

Work even in stockinette in the round for 30 (31, 29, 34, __) rows/5½ (5½, 5¼, 6,__) inches, or until sleeve reaches your armpit.

3X (4X, 5X): work in stockinette for 2 (2, 2, __) rows.

Increase row: k1, m1k, knit to end.

Repeat increase row every row 4 (14, 18, __) times, then every 2 rows 19 (15, 13, __) times, working plain rows in stockinette. Total stitches: 64 (70, 72, __)

Work even in stockinette in the round for 34, __ rows/6, __ inches, or until sleeve reaches your armpit.

All sizes:

Begin working flat in stockinette.

Flat decrease:

NOTE: All decreases are worked on one side of the garment, along the bottom edge of the back.

XS (S, M, L, 1X):

Row 1 (ws): p2tog, p to end.
Row 2 (rs): k to end.
Row 3 (ws): p to end.
Row 4 (rs): knit to last two stitches, k2tog.
Row 5 (ws): p to end.
Row 6 (rs): k to end.

Repeat these six rows two more times. Total stitches: 34 (34, 36, 40, 44, __)

2X (3X, 4X):

Row 1 (ws): p2tog, p to end.
Row 2 (rs): k to end.

Repeat these two rows 8 (7, 2,__) more times.

Row 1 (ws): p2tog, p to end.
Row 2 (rs): knit to last two stitches, k2tog.

Repeat these two rows 0 (3, 8, __) more times. Total stitches: 47 (49, 49, __)

5X:

Row 1 (ws): p2tog, p to end.
Row 2 (rs): knit to last two stitches, k2tog.

Repeat these two rows 10 more times. Total stitches: 50

Straight:

Work flat in stockinette for 13¾ (14¾, 15¾, 16¾, 17¼, 18½, 18½, 18½, 18½, __) inches/77 (81,

87, 93, 95, 103, 103, 103, 103, __) rows, ending with a ws row.

Flat Increase:
XS (S, M, L, 1X):
Row 1 (rs): knit to last stitch, m1k, k1.
Row 2 (ws): p to end.
Row 3 (rs): k to end.
Row 4 (ws): pfb, p to end.
Row 5 (rs): k to end.
Row 6 (ws): p to end.

Repeat these six rows two more times.
Total stitches: 40 (40, 42, 46, 50, __)

2X (3X, 4X):
Row 1 (rs): knit to last stitch, m1k, k1.
Row 2 (ws): pfb, p to end.

Repeat these two rows 0 (3, 8, __) more times.

Row 1 (rs): knit to last stitch, m1k, k1.
Row 2 (ws): p to end.

Repeat these two rows 8 (6, 2, __) more times. Total stitches: 58 (64, 70, __)

5X:
Row 1 (rs): knit to last stitch, m1k, k1.
Row 2 (ws): pfb, p to end.

Repeat these two rows 10 more times. Total stitches: 72

All sizes:
Rejoin to work in the round.
Work in stockinette for 11½ (12, 5½, 5½, 5¼, 6, 6, 6, 6, __) inches/63 (66, 30, 31, 29, 34, 34, 34, 34, __) rows, or until the straight section of the sleeve matches the straight section of the other sleeve.

Sleeve Decrease:
XS and S: No decreases, proceed to cuff instructions.
M (L, 1X, 2X):
Decrease row: k1, k2tog, knit to end.
Repeat decrease row every 32 (7, 4, 2, __) rows 1 (5, 9, 17, __) more time(s), working plain rows in stockinette. Total stitches: 40
Work in stockinette for 10 (8, 4, 4, __) rows.

3X (4X, 5X):
Decrease row: k1, k2tog, knit to end.
Repeat decrease row every row 4 (14, 18,_) times, then every 2 rows 19 (15, 13, __) times, working

plain rows in stockinette. Total stitches : 40
Work in stockinette for 2 (2, 2, __) rows.

Cuff:
P1 round.
K2, p1, *k1, p1,* rep between * to last 3 sts, k3.

Increase rows:
Row 1: k2, m1k, p1, *k1, p1,* rep between * to last 3, k1, m1p, k2.
Row 2: k2, *k1, p1,* rep between * to last 2, k2.
Row 3: k2, m1p, *k1, p1,* rep between * to last 2, m1k, k2.
Row 4: k1, *k1, p1,* rep between * to last 3, k3.

Repeat these four rows once more, then rows 1-3 once. Total stitches: 52

P1, *k1, p1,* rep between * to last st, k1.
Work in established pattern for 4".
Bind off using knit bind off in pattern.

Body:
In MC, with rs facing, pick up 84 (88, 92, 96, 98, 108, 109, 110, 102, __) stitches along bottom edge, starting at left armpit, then pick up 84 (88, 92, 96, 98, 108, 109, 110, 102, __) stitches along top edge. Total stitches: 168 (176, 184, 192, 196, 216, 218, 220, 220, __)

Join to work in the round, placing marker at beginning of round.
rs: purl 1 round.
Work in k1, p1 rib for 9 rounds.

On the next round, continue to work in k1, p1 rib, and place a marker after you have worked 110 (114, 118, 122, 122, 138, 138, 138, 136, __) stitches. This will be the right front collar edge. Continue working, and place a second marker when there are 20 (22, 24, 26, 28, 30, 30, 32, 34, __) stitches left in the round. This will be the left front collar edge.

Short Rows:
rs: continue in rib pattern as established until you reach the first marker. Remove marker. Turn work, do not wrap.
ws: work in rib pattern (working the last stitch completed again for this row) to round marker. Remove marker. Continue in rib pattern until you reach the second marker placed in the previous round. Remove marker. Turn work, do not wrap.

Work in established pattern to 1 stitch before previous turn. Turn work, do not wrap.

Repeat this row 94 (94, 94, 92, 92, 94, 96, 100, 106, __) times, 47 (47, 47, 46, 46, 47, 48, 50, 53, __) times each side or until sweater tail is the desired length. The pattern tail is designed to end mid-hip.

Bind Off:

In CC, with rs facing, slip last stitch worked onto crochet hook. Using single crochet, work the next stitch on the left needle. This results in one stitch bound off.

Continue binding off all stitches on the needle loosely, using single crochet.

Use a slip stitch to connect last stitch with first stitch. Sew in ends.

The Master and Commander
Cap and Cowl

By: Aimee Skeers

DESCRIPTION:
Sturdy and rugged, with gull-wing cables and a gear-tooth picot bind off, this cozy cap and cowl set will keep you warm and comfortable on all your adventures, without ever getting in your way.

FINISHED DIMENSIONS:
Hat circumference: to fit 21"
Cowl circumference: to fit 16"

GAUGE:
Knitted and blocked gauge:
In pattern on larger needles: 31 sts x 30 rows = 4"/10cm

YARN AND YARDAGE:
Silk/Cashmere Worsted by Hedgehog Fibres,
http://www.hedgehogfibres.com
50% silk, 50% Merino; 218yds (200m) per 100g; worsted weight
Color: Implode, 2 skeins

Be it of her own Airship, or her own destiny, a Lady knows that she alone is Master and Commander, and truly answers only to herself. However, maintaining this countenance through inclement conditions is far easier when sporting warm accessories that show your fashion sense, as well as your authority.

NEEDLES AND NOTIONS:
24" size 3 US/3.25mm circular needle
24" size 5 US/3.75mm circular needle
One set size 5 US/3.75mm dpns or long circular for magic loop
7 buttons
Tapestry needle
Waste yarn
Stitch markers

PATTERN/CHART NOTES:
The cap and cowl share the same cable chart. The cap is knit in the round, so each row is knit right to left. The cowl is knitted flat, so the chart rows will alternate right to left on rs rows and left to right on ws rows.

Pattern

Cowl

Using waste yarn and larger needles, CO 142 sts using a provisional CO. Slip the first stitch of every row as if to purl. Sl1, k1, work Row 1, working marked pattern repeat four times, then the rest of the charted row, end k2.

Next row: sl1, p1, continue on to Row 2 of chart, which will be a ws row, end p2. This two stitch border on the button bands is not charted.

To work buttonholes, on the second time you work Row 2 and every second Row 2 thereafter: p2, yo, p2tog, work in pattern to end.

Continue as set until piece measures 5 inches or desired height, ending on Row 2 of chart.

BO with a picot edge as follows: NOTE: For the picot bind off, cast on sts using the cable cast on method. After each BO set, slip the st on the right needle back to the left needle before you CO more sts.

BO 2, CO 2 sts, BO 8, CO 2 sts, BO 8, CO 2 sts, BO 6, CO 2 sts, BO 8, CO 2 sts, BO 7, CO 2 sts, BO 6, rep between * 4 more times. End CO 2 sts, BO 8, CO 2 sts, BO 10, CO 2 sts, BO 4.

Remove provisional CO, picking up sts. BO sts as before. The stitch counts will need to be fudged slightly because the stitches left over from the provisional CO won't match up perfectly with the stitches on the top edge. The important thing is to try to match the location of the picots as closely as possible.

FINISHING:
Sew 5 buttons on button band, matching buttonholes on other side. Weave in ends. Block, but be careful not to stretch the ribbed sections between the cables, or you will lose the elasticity that will keep the cowl snug against your neck

Cap

Using smaller circular needles, CO 140 sts and join to work in the round, pm.

Work in 2x2 rib for 1".

On next round: *(k2, p2) 4 times, (k1, m1k, k1, p2) 3 times,* rep between * around. 15 sts increased, 155 sts total.

Switch to larger needles and work marked section of chart for 4 inches from ribbing, ending with Row 2. (Marked section will repeat 5 times.)

Begin decreases as follows, switching to dpns or magic loop as necessary:

Round 1: *k2, p2, k2tog, sl2 wyib, ssk, p2, k2, p2, k2tog, k9, ssk, p2,* rep to end.

Round 2: *k2, p2, k1, sl2 wyib, k1, p2, k2, p2, k11, p2,* rep to end.

Round 3: *k2, p2, 1/1 rc, 1/1 lc, p2, k2, p2, 3/2 rc, k1, 3/2 lc, p2,* rep to end.

Round 4: knit the knits, purl the purls.

Round 5: *k2tog, p2, k1, sl2 wyib, k1, p2, k2tog, p2, k2tog, k7, ssk, p2,* rep to end.

Round 6: *k1, p2, k1, sl2 wyib, k1, p2, k1, p2, k9, p2,* rep to end.

Round 7: *k1, p2, 1/1 rc, 1/1 lc, p2, k1, p2, 2/2 rc, k1, 2/2 lc, p2,* rep to end.

Round 8: knit the knits, purl the purls.

Round 9: *k1, p2tog, k1, sl2 wyib, k1, p2tog, k1, p2tog, k2tog, k5, ssk, p2tog,* rep to end.

Round 10: *k1, p1, k1, sl2 wyib, k1, p1, k1, p1, k7, p1,* rep to end.

Round 11: *k1, p1, 1/1 rc, 1/1 lc, p1, k1, p1, 2/1 rc, k1, 2/1 lc, p1,* rep to end, but on last repeat do not work final purl stitch! On the next round this st joins the first p3tog.

Round 12: *p3tog, k2tog, ssk, p3tog, k2tog, k3, ssk,* rep to end.

Round 13: knit the knits, purl the purls.

Round 14: *p1, k2tog, p1, k2tog, k1, ssk,* rep to end.

Round 15: *p3tog, k3tog,* rep to end.

Break yarn, leaving an eight inch tail. Pass yarn through remaining 10 sts and weave in end.

To knit brim, use larger needles and pu 13 sts at cast on edge below one of the large herringbone cable ribs with rs facing you. Turn work and p13, pm, pu and k 2 sts from base of rib, turn. Sl1, p back to end, pm, pu and k 2 sts from base, turn.

rs: sl1, k to first marker, m1k, sm, k to second marker, sm, m1k, k to end, pu and k 2 more sts from base.

ws: sl1, p to end, pu and p 2 more sts from base.

Repeat these two rows four times more. Purl the next two rows, slipping first st on each.

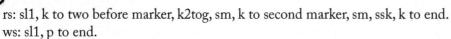

rs: sl1, k to two before marker, k2tog, sm, k to second marker, sm, ssk, k to end.
ws: sl1, p to end.

Repeat these two rows four times more. BO, leaving a 12 inch tail. Sew BO edge to inside edge of brim.

To knit strap, CO 6 sts using larger needles. Starting on Row 2 of the chart, work the strap using just stitches 5-10 of the chart, repeating rows 2-5 until strap measures 7 inches. Bind off.

Sew to hat, centered just above brim. Sew one button to each end of strap.

Chart

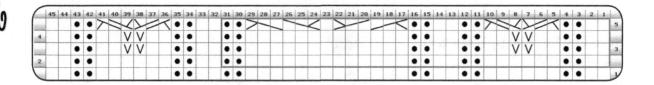

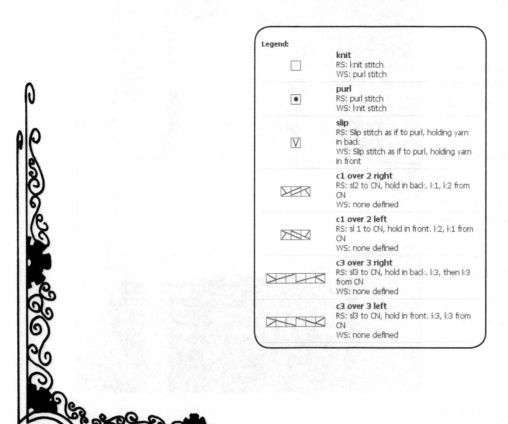

Legend:

	knit
☐	RS: knit stitch WS: purl stitch
⊡	**purl** RS: purl stitch WS: knit stitch
Ⅴ	**slip** RS: Slip stitch as if to purl, holding yarn in back WS: Slip stitch as if to purl, holding yarn in front
	c1 over 2 right RS: sl2 to CN, hold in back. k1, k2 from CN WS: none defined
	c1 over 2 left RS: sl 1 to CN, hold in front. k2, k1 from CN WS: none defined
	c3 over 3 right RS: sl3 to CN, hold in back. k3, then k3 from CN WS: none defined
	c3 over 3 left RS: sl3 to CN, hold in front. k3, k3 from CN WS: none defined

Chapter Four

In which the Ladies meet some surprising residents at the farm

Mrs. Miriam Tingley was in her office in the haybarn when her brooch began chiming. She jumped, scattering the tiny papers she was arranging. "Blast! Now I'm going to have to redo the breeding plans, and my experiment is going to have to wait. How do the Ladies keep getting in so much trouble?" Continuing her grumbling, she wrote down the brooch message, then found the folder for her current experiment. Her test of the theories of the upstart scientist Darwin would have to wait. She was underneath her desk looking for the last scraps of paper when she saw Theodosia in the doorway.

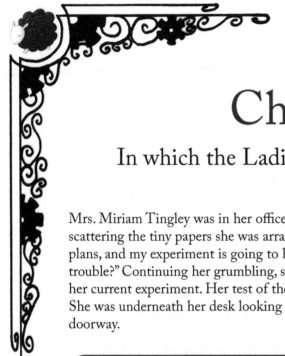

Mrs. Miriam Tingley was the Ladies' financial manager and owner of Tingley Ranch. She had been severely challenged at a young age, first losing her husband at sea within their first year of marriage, then suffering the tragedy of losing her entire family when a runaway automaton destroyed the Philadelphia tea room they were visiting. Two distressing events, within a single year, but she did not collapse in nervous hysteria as many women would. She raised her chin and put her not-inconsiderable smarts to work on the family farm. The farm flourished under her care, and the settlement from the automaton's owner provided her an opportunity for expansion. Her business acumen and bravery lead her to invest in the New Western Territory of Montana, purchasing a large swath of high country from a bankrupt cattleman. Her newly-founded sheep ranch grew quickly, and Tingley Ranch Yarns became known as some of the finest wool in America. Mrs. Miriam Tingley's remote location belied her central role in the affairs of the Ladies. She managed the Ladies' combined fortunes, patents, products, and papers, helping those more interested in discovery to gain benefit from their work.

"Did you hear it? Do you think Anna's all right?! What is she going to do now?!" Theodosia's eyes were wide and she was panting a little from the run in from the far pasture.

"Don't worry, the Ladies will take care of her." Miriam smiled broadly. "And now the adventure is just getting started. Get ready to head out soon!"

Theodosia smiled and began bouncing slightly on her feet. "Sounds like fun! I'll get packed!"

****

"Attention everyone!" Coraline's voice boomed through the airship. "We'll be landing at the Tingley Ranch in ten minutes! If you look over the starboard railing you can see the stunning hot springs of the Yellowstone Basin."

The Ladies rushed to the deck to view the sights, leaving knitting and teacups stranded in the captain's cabin. "Why, look at those colors!" Alyssa pointed to the vivid orange ring around the deep blue water of one of the springs. "They would be extremely striking in a qipao pattern! I must contact my dyer immediately."

Kristoff checked his pocket watch and sighed. Hot springs and silk dyers were all well and good, but he needed to get to London. Anna reached

over and squeezed his hand and was about to whisper to him when a blast of warm steam flooded the deck.

"Oh! I forgot to mention that we would be passing over the most vigorous steam spout." Coraline's voice held a hint of laughter. "Now that everyone's refreshed, it's time to prepare for landing." The bubbling pools passed behind them as the Ladies put on shawls and collected their wayward knitting.

The airship landed with the gentlest bump, and the gangplank was lowered onto verdant fields. "Why hello, Ladies, and welcome to my ranch!" A friendly voice rang through the clear mountain air. As the Ladies broached the gangplank, they were greeted by the proud smile of Mrs. Miriam Tingley.

Mrs. Tingley's ranch, nestled in the mountains of Montana, was breathtaking in beauty. It consisted of five large barns and one cozy cabin, surrounded by several rolling pastures. Miriam kept multiple flocks of sheep, combining the best aspects of several breeds into her acclaimed yarn. One entire barn was devoted to her Fine Fleece Finishing Mechanism, a giant machine that could skirt, wash and card fleeces in preparation for spinning. Her spinning operation took up another barn, though the machines were much smaller. She kept her handspinning wheels in there as well, next to a tiny kitchen that was well-stocked with tea. Her handspun yarn was only produced when she had a moment to sit, and therefore was a rare delight, much sought after by the Ladies.

As the Ladies descended the gangplank onto the front field, Miriam counted them with glee. "How wonderful to see so many of you all together! What adventure brings you to my mountain?"

"Miriam!" Anna leapt into the older woman's arms for a firm hug. "It's been simply ages! How is the ranch?"

Miriam laughed and removed Anna's cap to ruffle the red hair underneath. "Enthusiastic as ever, I see! The ranch is splendid! Better than ever! But you must introduce me to your companion properly." The two turned to face Kristoff, Anna pulling her hat back on.

"Mrs. Miriam Tingley, may I present Kristoff Von Boltenstein?" Anna grinned broadly as the two shook hands. Miriam always shook hands properly, she reflected, going for a firm grim and a good shake. "Miriam takes care of the finances for the Ladies, and does a bloody good job at it. She also runs this lovely ranch! I really don't visit the Americas often enough..." Anna trailed off, staring off at the mountainous vista with a sigh.

"Oh, and Kristoff has joined me on the airship of late. He's a dab hand at making cheese toast. Also, he kisses extremely well." Anna didn't see a problem with divulging this bit of information, while Kristoff blushed and the rest of the Ladies snickered.

Miriam smiled warmly, ignoring Kristoff's blush, and shook his hand. "Very pleased to meet you, Kristoff. Welcome to the Tingley Ranch!" She released his hand and turned to the rest of the group. "Now, then, what has brought you all to my doorstep? My brooch chimed days ago, something about a crash landing?"

Several Ladies began talking at once, but it was Anna's voice that rose above them all. She recounted their adventure thus far in increasingly angry and aggrieved tones until it must be said that she was, in fact, shouting. Miriam took it in stride, choosing to shout her responses and questions as well to keep in the spirit of things. The nearby ranch hands glanced over, then pretended to continue their tasks as they listened. The commotion drew an amused looking gentleman out of one of the barns.

"Mr. Tingley!" Coraline's voice somehow cut through the hubbub, "Come on over and give me your report on our newest device!"

The Ladies settled down as the gentleman strolled over and bowed. "Miss Hackworth, I believe it's working even better than we expected!"

Charles Tingley was the Chief Engineer for Hackworth Airships International, and much of his best work was carried out in the Green Barn on the Tingley Ranch. His sister-in-law Miriam provided him space and seclusion to work on secret experimental projects. The industrial spies attempting to discover Hackworth technology were quite frustrated by the company's ability to produce new inventions seemingly out of thin air. Charles, for his part, enjoyed the privacy and the rugged landscape of the ranch, almost as far as possible from the sea that claimed his brother's life. He had been working on a very advanced device when Coraline contacted him before heading to Shanghai, and he was ready to begin the test phase.

Charles briefly exchanged pleasantries with the Ladies then spent several moments in quiet conversation with Coraline. Her serious expression grew

more excited by the moment, and by the time he politely excused himself to begin upgrading the airship, she was nearly beaming. All the Ladies' questions about "the device" were left unanswered, with a slightly smug Coraline insisting that they must see it in action to truly understand it.

Miriam had some idea of the nature of the device, but could keep a secret better than most. And she had a secret of her own to share, so she deftly turned the conversation. "Ladies, I think you are going to be very surprised by my latest flock. I have them hidden in the back pasture. Let's go take a look, shall we?" Miriam was nearly bursting with excitement. The Ladies were intrigued, and proceeded much faster than usual through the ranch. Which is to say, they only stopped to:

Look at three different flower specimens,
Admire the view of the mountains,
Discuss the difficulty of air travel in a high wind environment,
Sight a wolf stalking the pasture (Anna won five pounds from Coraline by managing to scare it away with a thrown rock), and
Discuss the necessity of sturdy footwear when traversing a large distance of pasture.
Kristoff sighed, and managed to keep his pocketwatch in his pocket by sheerest will.

As the group climbed the small hill that protected the most valuable flocks, the outline of a figure seated on a fallen tree writing in a journal appeared. Alyssa jumped forward in surprise. "My dear Theodosia! How lovely to see you again! But whatever are you doing so far inland?"

"Yes, didn't you leave for the Amazon not too long ago?" Anna asked with a curious frown. "I've been out of contact with the Ladies, so I'm not sure what happened after that."

Theodosia grinned up at them, her eyes alight with mischievous joy and her fingers smudged with ink. "Oh! My Ladies! I have the most remarkable news! On my expedition into the jungle, we made the most amazing discovery!" Anna smiled at Theodosia's exuberance, which was contagious. The Ladies leaned closer. "I was chasing a most singular beetle when it dove beneath a bush. I reached after it, but I prodded something soft and warm instead! I pushed the leaves aside and you will never guess what I found!"

"Another beetle?"

"A jaguar?"

"The long-lost Amazon Arnicular Armitata mushroom?" Everyone stopped to stare at Caldonia, even the slightly dazed ranch hands that were escorting her over the rough terrain. She shrugged. "It's what I would have hoped for."

"No, you silly people. It was a sheep! Perfectly adapted to life in the Amazon! With the most delightful camouflage and the sweetest little baa! They were quite unafraid of us, so I was able to begin some tests with their wonderful wool. The crimp! The luster! Oh! Ladies! I almost never want to knit with anything else. You must see them in person, they're remarkable!" She stood, stowing her pen and journal in the satchel on her belt, next to a small machete.

Anna raised an eyebrow. "So we'll all just set out for the Amazon, then, and you can show us where they live? Because that is a touch far…"

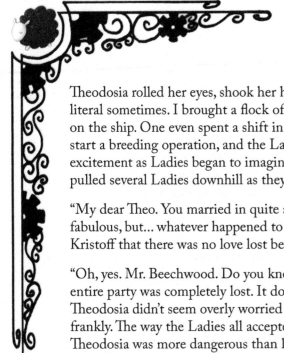

Theodosia rolled her eyes, shook her head, and even stamped her foot. "Oh, Anna. You are so literal sometimes. I brought a flock of them back with me! They adapted quite amazingly to travel on the ship. One even spent a shift in the crow's nest with the lookout! Miriam and I intend to start a breeding operation, and the Ladies will get the first batch of fiber!" There was a murmur of excitement as Ladies began to imagine what they would knit with such unusual yarn. Theodosia pulled several Ladies downhill as they chatted.

"My dear Theo. You married in quite a rush just before you left for the Amazon. Your dress was quite fabulous, but... whatever happened to your dear husband?" The slightest sneer in Alyssa's voice told Kristoff that there was no love lost between any of the Ladies and Theodosia's spouse.

"Oh, yes. Mr. Beechwood. Do you know, it seems he tried to follow me into the Amazon and his entire party was completely lost. It does so often happen when one goes into the jungle unprepared." Theodosia didn't seem overly worried about her missing husband. She seemed fairly smug about it, frankly. The way the Ladies all accepted this statement without question made Kristoff realize that Theodosia was more dangerous than her small frame implied. The sun glinted off the machete she carried, and he made a note to never get on her bad side.

"Ah, here we are!" Theodosia stopped before a small forest and gestured expansively. "They're quite at home living in trees and bushes. Miriam has the perfect area for them here! Just try to find them!" The Ladies all fanned out, searching among the brush.

"Oooh! I found one!" Caldonia exclaimed. "Ahem, I mean, its camouflage ability is quite impressive." Her escorts nodded sagely.

"Baaaa, Baaaa, Baaaa" Coraline commanded. There was no response. She cleared her throat and used her most impressive captain voice, "BAAAA!". A tiny sheep leaped out of the bushes and stood at attention in front of her. Coraline held her posture for a moment before dropping to her knees in delight. "Oh, at ease little one. Good show!"

"Now Cora, the sheep have only had a week to adjust to life here. I hardly think it's appropriate to drill them now." Miriam sent a pointed look to Coraline.

"Don't worry, Miriam, they rather enjoy loud sounds." Theodosia chimed in. "I believe that they might miss the simian screams of the jungle. Cora here is merely helping them feel at home."

Coraline's cheeks turned red as the words sank in. Theodosia eyed her carefully, and was bracing for a very loud lecture when Coraline burst into laughter. The rest of the Ladies merrily joined in and the joyous sound brought the remainder of the sheep from their hiding places. Anna picked up a chestnut brown one and placed it on her shoulders. The wee sheep perched there happily and attempted to eat her hat. "They're delightful! I want this one!" She rubbed noses with the little sheep while Kristoff looked on with an amused smile.

The Ladies spent several minutes in sheep admiration, discussing their unique qualities and their wonderfully diminutive size.

"The hand of this wool is remarkable. I believe it could be used to make fabulously decadent undergarments." Alyssa had a slightly wicked grin as she petted the sheep. "Perhaps the heat of the jungle will help to promote...heat...in the wearer." Some of the Ladies grinned slyly, while others chose this moment to inspect their respective sheep quite closely.

Miriam whipped a large notebook out of her satchel. "I've begun to work on a breeding plan that I believe will maintain their best characteristics, while giving them better hardiness to handle our winters here! You see, we have eight ewes, and two rams, and if we begin by pairing the two stoutest..." A bell began ringing back at the cabin, interrupting what was sure to be a long and detailed explanation. Miriam visibly restrained herself and put away her notebook. "Well, that plan can wait. Allright everyone, our picnic lunch should be ready! Follow me!"

"A picnic?" Kristoff asked. He pulled out his pocketwatch and checked the time. Yes. Time to get to London, he thought! Anna smiled at him and stood on her tiptoes to give him a gentle kiss. The little sheep on her shoulders nosed at his ear in a friendly manner.

"I know, love. The Ladies of Mischief are the most solid, reliable and amazing women I know... But we do tend to take our time with things." She set the little chestnut sheep down and linked her arm through his. "It's a lovely day here in the Americas, though. And we definitely need to eat." They walked arm-in-arm through the Tingley field to where a lovely luncheon was laid out. Several sheep stood nearby, hopeful that one of those baskets would hold grain.

Kristoff sighed. The corner of his mouth twitched into a small smile. "Is Mrs. Tingley really insisting on bringing some of the jungle sheep?"

Anna grinned. "Oh, yes. She is certain that they'll come in handy. She says you never know when you'll need a sheep around to eat something, headbutt something, or defecate on something. And they're small, at least. I find them quite endearing."

Kristoff shook his head. "Your friends are all mad."

"Yes. And I love them for it. Come on!" She pulled him the last few yards to the picnickers, and leaped bodily into the center of the blankets. "Where are the tiny sandwiches? I specifically requested tiny sandwiches!" Kristoff watched her for a moment with a smile on his face. Caldonia noticed him and offered him a cup of tea and a welcoming grin.

"You're never getting rid of us now, you know." She passed him the cup, and he laughed a little as he took it.

"I know. The idea has been growing on me." Kristoff smiled and settled himself down on the picnic blankets, pushing the nose of the tiny chestnut sheep away from his cup of tea. "Now, then," he said. "I heard something about tiny sandwiches?"

The Mountain Lily Scarf
By: Heidi Kunkel

DESCRIPTION:
This is a lace scarf inspired by an Estonian stitch, the 3-into-9 star.

SPECIAL TECHNIQUES:
3-into-9 star: k3tog, but don't pull the stitch off your left needle. *Yo, k3tog into same stitches again,* repeat between * 4 times, until there are 9 stitches on your right needle, then slip the stitches from the left needle. On the next wrong side row, purl each of these 9 stitches individually.

YARN AND YARDAGE:
Extra Fine Lace by Epicurus, http://epicurus.etsy.com
70% baby alpaca, 20% silk, and 10% cashmere; 600yds (549m) per 50g; lace weight
Color: Cactus Bud, 1 skein

GAUGE:
Knitted and blocked gauge:
In stockinette: 19½ sts x 30 rows = 4"/10cm

In the wilds of Montana blooms the Mountain Lily. Never too fussy, but always elegant, this delicate floral scarf reminds us that a touch of beauty always has a place, even in the most rustic settings.

NEEDLES AND NOTIONS:
16" or longer size 6 US/3.5mm circular needle (straight needles will work fine if they are long enough to accommodate all of your stitches).

PATTERN NOTES:

This scarf is knit with a garter stitch border. Pattern repeat stitch count changes back and forth from 12 to 14 stitches over the course of a 16 row repeat.

Loosely cast on 45 sts.

Pattern

Knit 6 rows in garter stitch to establish edge.

Work chart, repeating rows 1-16 until desired length (ending with row 16). For reference, scarf pictured contains 43 repeats for a total length of 108 inches.

Knit 6 rows in garter stitch, bind off loosely.

CHART NOTES:

Knit the first and last 3 stitches of every row. Chart does not include these 6 edge stitches. Repeat the outlined section of the chart one time (or more if you choose to add repeats to your width) before working remainder of the row.

FINISHING:

Weave in ends and block vigorously to flatten out the 3-into-9 stars. To get the rippled edge as pictured, use at least 3 pins per flower to avoid getting points. This requires 6 pins per 16-row repeat, plus extra for the edges.

Chart

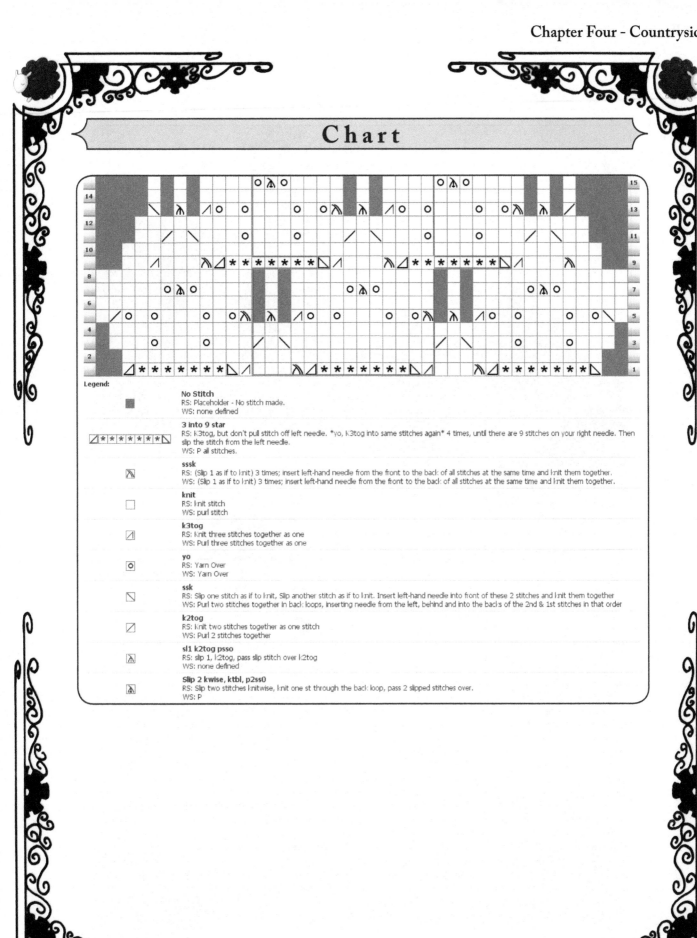

Legend:

No Stitch
RS: Placeholder - No stitch made.
WS: none defined

3 into 9 star
RS: k3tog, but don't pull stitch off left needle. *yo, k3tog into same stitches again* 4 times, until there are 9 stitches on your right needle. Then slip the stitch from the left needle.
WS: P all stitches.

sssk
RS: (Slip 1 as if to knit) 3 times; insert left-hand needle from the front to the back of all stitches at the same time and knit them together.
WS: (Slip 1 as if to knit) 3 times; insert left-hand needle from the front to the back of all stitches at the same time and knit them together.

knit
RS: knit stitch
WS: purl stitch

k3tog
RS: Knit three stitches together as one
WS: Purl three stitches together as one

yo
RS: Yarn Over
WS: Yarn Over

ssk
RS: Slip one stitch as if to knit, Slip another stitch as if to knit. Insert left-hand needle into front of these 2 stitches and knit them together
WS: Purl two stitches together in back loops, inserting needle from the left, behind and into the backs of the 2nd & 1st stitches in that order

k2tog
RS: knit two stitches together as one stitch
WS: Purl 2 stitches together

sl1 k2tog psso
RS: slip 1, k2tog, pass slip stitch over k2tog
WS: none defined

Slip 2 kwise, ktbl, p2ss0
RS: Slip two stitches knitwise, knit one st through the back loop, pass 2 slipped stitches over.
WS: P

The Warm and Tingley
Headscarf and Mitts
By: Heidi Kunkel

DESCRIPTION:

Headscarf: Cabled headband that buttons at the nape of the neck, making a great accessory to keep your ears and forehead warm when you don't want to wear a full hat.

It can also double as a cowl if you button it tighter and wear it around your neck.

Mitts: Unisex cabled fingerless mitts, knit in the round, with a picot bind off and an afterthought thumb.

FINISHED DIMENSIONS:

Headscarf:

Length: 15" relaxed, 26" fully stretched

Height/Depth: 5" relaxed

Everyone on Mrs. Tingley's farmstead knows that whatever the weather, there's work to be done! From the first fall breezes through the brisk spring mornings, this headscarf and mitts are sure to keep you cozy. These quick knits are perfect for sharing the warmth with your dearest Ladies too.

Mitts:
Width: 6½" circumference around palm of hand, unstretched. These will stretch to fit a wide variety of hand sizes.
Length: 9¼"

YARN AND YARDAGE:
Shanti Worsted by Stone and String Studio,
http://www.ravelry.com/yarns/library/stone-and-string-shanti-worsted
80% Merino, 20% silk; 250yds (229m) per 100g; worsted weight
Color: Shanti, 1 skein total for both patterns

GAUGE:
Knitted and blocked gauge:
In stockinette: 18½ sts x 23 rows = 4"/10cm

NEEDLES AND NOTIONS:
Tapestry needle
Headscarf: 24" size 9 US/5.5mm circular needle
4 stitch markers (optional)
1 button (23 or 25mm, you may want to buy the button after you finish the project to determine which size you prefer.)
Mitts: 22" or longer size 9 US/5.5mm circular needle, or preferred needle(s) for working in the round
Waste yarn

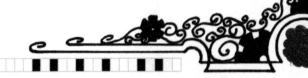

Headscarf

PATTERN NOTES:

This pattern is worked in short rows, decreasing in length for the first half, and then increasing in length for the second half. The short rows are worked by turning work at the symbol without wrapping them thus forming intentional holes in your knitting that are then used as buttonholes (you can use whichever hole fits your head size best).

CHART NOTES:

Rows 23, 25, and 27 on the Headscarf Chart have slightly different cables than the rest of the pattern to facilitate switching back to ribbing. Pay close attention.

Pattern

Using the long tail cast on method and stitch markers, cast on 82 stitches as follows:

Cast on 3, pm, cast on 18, pm, cast on 40, pm, cast on 18, pm, cast on 3.
The inside 2 markers do not move as you knit (they mark how far in the short rows go), but the outer 2 markers WILL move on most rows.

Follow the Headscarf Chart, turning your work when you get to the symbol.

Begin working chart as follows:

Rows 1-13:
For the first half of the headscarf, until the end of row 13 on the chart, you will knit in pattern to the outermost marker, remove marker, turn, work 3 stitches, pm, and continue across row.

Rows 14-15:
Work these two rows in pattern, turning at the end of each but without moving markers.

Rows 16-28:
For the second half of the headscarf, work in pattern to the outermost marker, remove marker, work 3 stitches, and THEN turn work and pm.

Upon completion of chart, bind off very loosely in pattern.

FINISHING:
Use your yarn tail to sew on your button, and then weave in one remaining end. Wear and enjoy!

Fingerless Mitts

SPECIAL TECHNIQUES :
Picot bind off, afterthought thumb

PATTERN NOTES:
These mitts are a simple tube of knitting with an afterthought thumb and a picot bind off. The palm side is a k2p1 rib, and the back side is cabled.

Pattern

Loosely cast on 36 stitches. Join to knit in the round, being careful not to twist.

Left Hand:
Work Left Hand Chart A one time.

Work Left Hand Chart B twice, ignoring shaded stitches. On third repeat of Chart B, work shaded thumb stitches as described at the end of the pattern. Work Chart B though a fourth time, working shaded stitches in pattern.

Work Left Hand Chart C one time.

Work picot bind off as follows:
Bind off 5 stitches. *Slip 1 stitch from right needle back to left needle, cast on 1 stitch using cable cast on, bind off 7 stitches,* repeat between * 4 more times. Slip last stitch back to left needle, cast on 1 stitch using cable cast on, bind off last 2 stitches.

Right Hand:
Work as for Left Hand but with Right Hand Charts.
Bind off as for Left Hand.

Afterthought Thumb:

Work in pattern to the shaded stitches. Work these 6 stitches with waste yarn, slip them back to the left needle, and work them again with the working yarn before continuing across your row as usual.

After finishing the rest of the pattern, carefully unpick waste yarn to release live stitches for the thumb.

Pick up the 6 live stitches from the bottom edge and 5 stitches from the top edge.

Leaving enough of a yarn tail to close up the holes that will form, knit in pattern across 6 bottom stitches.

Pick up and knit 2 stitches in the gap between the lower and upper stitches.

Knit in pattern across top 5 stitches.

Pick up and knit 2 stitches in the gap between this and beginning of round. Total stitches: 15

Knit in pattern for 6 more rounds, then bind off loosely.

FINISHING:

Weave in ends, paying close attention to close holes formed by picking up stitches around thumb.

Charts

Headscarf

Chart rotated clockwise

Legend:

knit
RS: knit stitch
WS: purl stitch

purl
RS: purl stitch
WS: knit stitch

No Stitch
RS: Placeholder - No stitch made.
WS: none defined

Turn work
RS: Turn work and start working back.
WS: Turn work and start working back.

c2 over 2 right
RS: sl2 to CN, hold in back. k2, k2 from CN
WS: none defined

c2 over 2 left
RS: sl 2 to CN, hold in front. k2, k2 from CN
WS: none defined

c2 over 2 right P
RS: sl2 to CN, hold in back. k2, p2 from CN
WS: none defined

c2 over 2 left P
RS: sl 2 to CN, hold in front. p2, k2 from CN
WS: none defined

2/2 Right Cable with Purl
RS: Slip 2 to cable needle, hold to back, k1,
P1, K2 from cable needle.
WS:

2/2 Left Cable with Purl
RS: Slip 2 to cable needle, hold to front, k2,
P1, k1 from cable needle.
WS:

2/2 Right Cable with 2 Purls
RS: Slip next 2 sts to cable needle and hold in
back. P1, k1; k1, p1 from cable needle.
WS:

2/2 Left Cable with 2 Purls
RS: Slip 2 to cable needle, hold to front, P1,
k1; k1, P1 from cable needle.
WS:

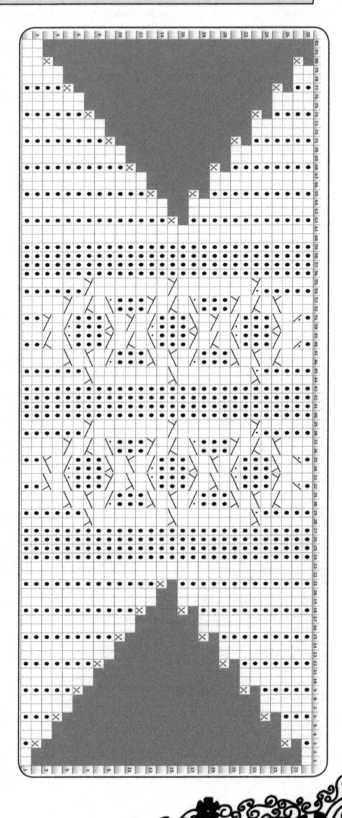

Mitts

Left Hand A

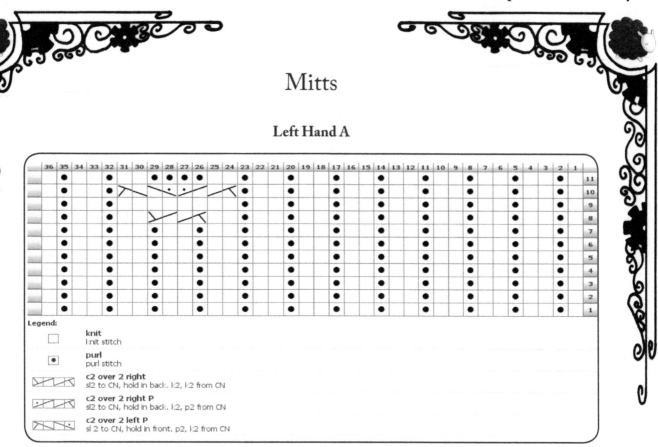

Legend:

	knit
	knit stitch
⊙	purl
	purl stitch
▨▨	c2 over 2 right
	sl2 to CN, hold in back. k2, k2 from CN
▨▨	c2 over 2 right P
	sl2 to CN, hold in back. k2, p2 from CN
▨▨	c2 over 2 left P
	sl 2 to CN, hold in front. p2, k2 from CN

Left Hand B

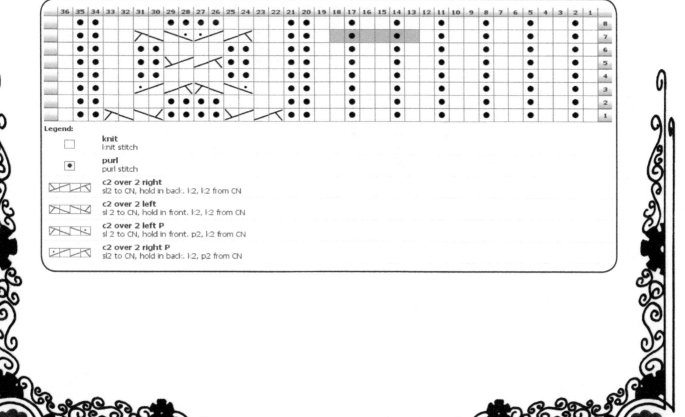

Legend:

	knit
	knit stitch
⊙	purl
	purl stitch
▨▨	c2 over 2 right
	sl2 to CN, hold in back. k2, k2 from CN
▨▨	c2 over 2 left
	sl 2 to CN, hold in front. k2, k2 from CN
▨▨	c2 over 2 left P
	sl 2 to CN, hold in front. p2, k2 from CN
▨▨	c2 over 2 right P
	sl2 to CN, hold in back. k2, p2 from CN

Mitts

Left Hand C

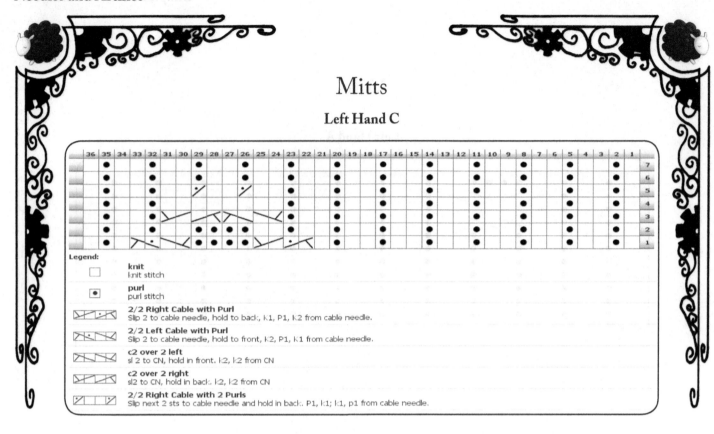

Legend:

☐	**knit**	knit stitch
⊡	**purl**	purl stitch
⧄	**2/2 Right Cable with Purl**	Slip 2 to cable needle, hold to back, k1, P1, k2 from cable needle.
⧄	**2/2 Left Cable with Purl**	Slip 2 to cable needle, hold to front, k2, P1, k1 from cable needle.
⧄	**c2 over 2 left**	sl 2 to CN, hold in front. k2, k2 from CN
⧄	**c2 over 2 right**	sl2 to CN, hold in back. k2, k2 from CN
⧄	**2/2 Right Cable with 2 Purls**	Slip next 2 sts to cable needle and hold in back. P1, k1; k1, p1 from cable needle.

Right Hand A

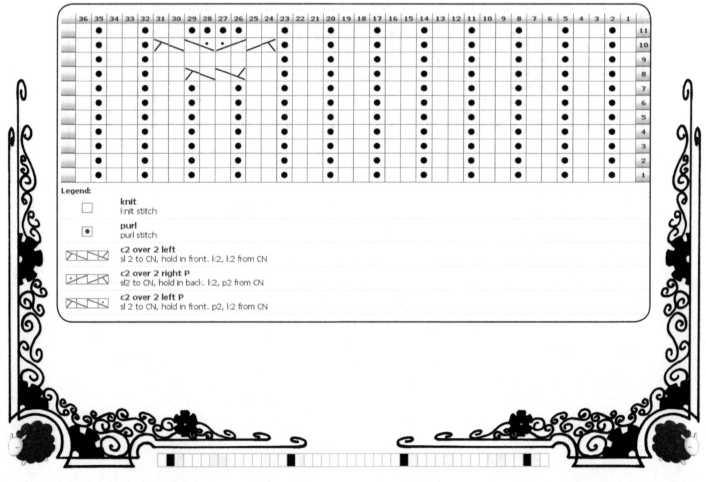

Legend:

☐	**knit**	knit stitch
⊡	**purl**	purl stitch
⧄	**c2 over 2 left**	sl 2 to CN, hold in front. k2, k2 from CN
⧄	**c2 over 2 right P**	sl2 to CN, hold in back. k2, p2 from CN
⧄	**c2 over 2 left P**	sl 2 to CN, hold in front. p2, k2 from CN

Mitts

Right Hand B

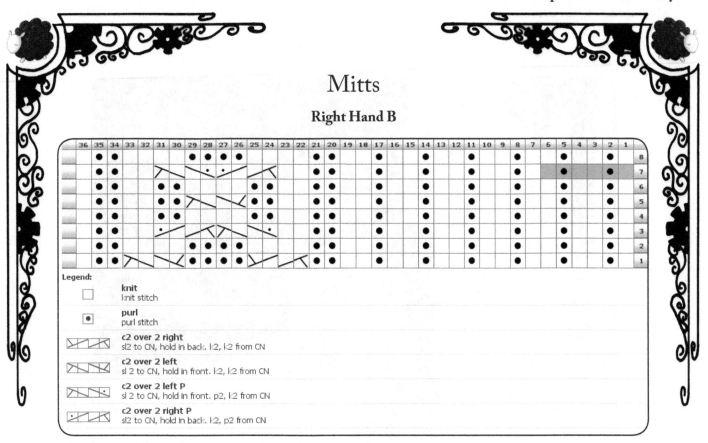

Legend:

	knit	
□	knit stitch	

	purl	
⊡	purl stitch	

| | c2 over 2 right | sl2 to CN, hold in back. k2, k2 from CN |

| | c2 over 2 left | sl 2 to CN, hold in front. k2, k2 from CN |

| | c2 over 2 left P | sl 2 to CN, hold in front. p2, k2 from CN |

| | c2 over 2 right P | sl2 to CN, hold in back. k2, p2 from CN |

Right Hand C

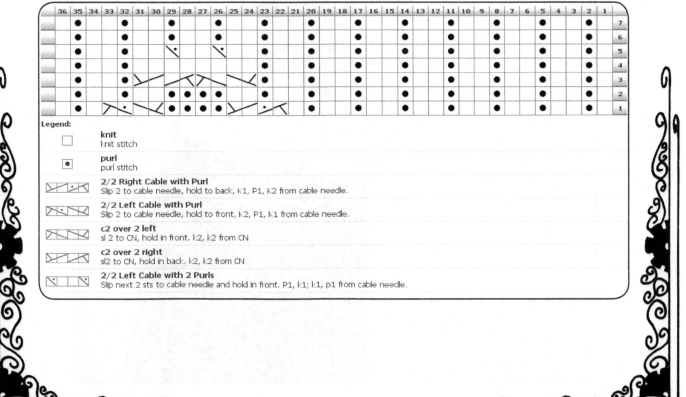

Legend:

	knit	
□	knit stitch	

	purl	
⊡	purl stitch	

| | 2/2 Right Cable with Purl | Slip 2 to cable needle, hold to back, k1, P1, k2 from cable needle. |

| | 2/2 Left Cable with Purl | Slip 2 to cable needle, hold to front, k2, P1, k1 from cable needle. |

| | c2 over 2 left | sl 2 to CN, hold in front. k2, k2 from CN |

| | c2 over 2 right | sl2 to CN, hold in back. k2, k2 from CN |

| | 2/2 Left Cable with 2 Purls | Slip next 2 sts to cable needle and hold in front. P1, k1; k1, p1 from cable needle. |

The Abundance Vest
By: Aimee Skeers

DESCRIPTION:

This top-down vest features a diagonal travelling cable across the entire front, creating a fabric that has characteristics of fabric knit on the bias. This stitch pattern creates a fabric that drapes and flatters the curves of the body, while the ribbed back provides fit.

YARN AND YARDAGE:

Regale by Fiberstory,
http://fiberstory.etsy.com
80% merino, 10% cashmere, 10% nylon; 181yds (165m) per 113g; aran weight
Color: Ha'penny, 4 (5, 7, 8, 9, 10) skeins

The Tingley Ranch is a beacon of abundance and prosperity with dense gardens and exotic flocks. And though a true sense of abundance starts from within, a little help from a well shaped garment can subtly flatter the external sense of abundance as well.

GAUGE:

Knitted and blocked gauge:
In stockinette: 20 sts x 28 rows = 4"/10cm
In pattern: 24 sts x 32 rows = 4"/10cm
In 2x2 rib pattern: 28 sts x 26 rows = 4"/10cm

NEEDLES AND NOTIONS:

One set size 7 US/4.5mm needles

FINISHED DIMENSIONS:

Bust: 31¼ (33½, 38¾, 43½, 48¼, 51)"

EASE:

1-3" negative ease

TO FIT BODY MEASUREMENTS:

Bust: 32 (36, 40, 44, 50, 54)"

PATTERN NOTES:

This pattern is designed with negative ease, so the finished measurements are expected to be smaller than the wearer's measurements. Most of the negative ease comes from the 2x2 ribbing across the back. Swatching and testing the stretched and unstretched measurements will help you to chose the correct size if you are between sizes.

Pattern

Vest Shoulder Straps, Worked at the Same Time:
CO 19 (23, 27, 31, 35, 39) sts.
With a new ball of yarn, CO 19 (23, 27, 31, 35, 39) sts again.
P one row.
K one row.

Pattern Setup Row:
P2, k3, *p1, k3* to last 2 sts, p2.
Begin working Strap One and Strap Two charts. Please note that the cable pattern requires changing some stitches from k to p or from p to k during the cable crossings **(See Strap One/Strap Two Charts)**.

Increase Row:
After working 4 (4½, 5, 5½, 6, 6½) repeats of Strap One and Strap Two charts.
Strap One: work in pattern to last 2 sts, m1pwise, k2.
Strap Two: k2, m1pwise, work in pattern to end.

Repeat this increase on every odd row for 3 (3, 4, 4, 5, 5) repeats of chart.
24 (24, 32, 32, 40, 40) sts increased on inner neck.
31 (35, 43, 47, 55, 59) sts on each side after increases.

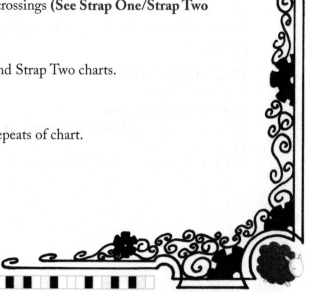

On next rs row, on **Strap One**: k1, m1, work in pattern to last 2 sts, m1pwise, k2. On **Strap Two**: k2, m1pwise, work in pattern to last st, m1, k1. Continue to increase like this on every odd row for 2½ (2½, 2½, 3, 3, 3) chart repeats, ending with Row 4 or Row 8 of pattern.

40 (40, 40, 48, 48, 48) sts increased total.

51 (55, 63, 71, 79, 83) sts on either side after increases.

Join to Create Front of Vest:

Starting with either Row 5 or Row 1 of chart (depending on if you ended on Row 4 or 8 previously), work in pattern (no increases) to the last 2 sts of first shoulder strap, k2tog.

With same yarn, ssk first two sts of second shoulder strap, work in pattern to end.

100 (108, 124, 140, 156, 164) sts total.

At this point you may break the yarn from the second ball.

Begin working Vest Body Chart from your current row number. Work chart until vest measures 18 (20, 22, 24, 26, 28) inches from beginning of shoulder straps, ending on Row 8 of chart.

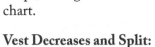

Vest Decreases and Split:
Begin decreases for bottom of vest as follows: k1, ssk, work in pattern to last three sts, k2tog, k1. Repeat this round every odd row for 1 (1, 1, 2, 2, 2) chart repeats.

Work rows 1-6 of Vest Body Chart. On the next row (Row 7 of the chart) work in pattern (including decreases) until the center 4 sts. K these 4 sts (do not cable them), then work in patten to end.

On the next row (Row 8), work in pattern to center 4 knit sts, p2, attach another ball of yarn, and work in pattern to end.

Vest Base Split:
Each odd row, k1, ssk, work in pattern to last 4 sts, k3tog, k1 on first vest base. On second vest base, k1, sssk, work in pattern to last 3 sts,

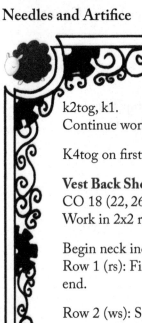

k2tog, k1.
Continue working this decrease row on every odd numbered row until four sts remain.

K4tog on first vest base, ssssk on second vest base. Pull yarn tail through last st to bind off.

Vest Back Shoulder Straps, Worked at the Same Time:
CO 18 (22, 26, 30, 34, 38) sts. Using a second ball of yarn, CO 18 (22, 26, 30, 34, 38) sts again.
Work in 2x2 rib for 1 (1, 1, 2, 2, 2) inches, ending with a ws row.

Begin neck increases as follows:
Row 1 (rs): First strap: work in pattern to last st, m1, k1. Second strap: k1, m1, work in pattern to end.

Row 2 (ws): Second strap: work in pattern to last 2 sts, m1pwise, p2. First strap: p2, m1pwise, work in pattern to end.

Row 3 (rs): First strap: work in pattern to last 2 sts, m1pwise, k2. Second strap: k2, m1pwise, work in pattern to end.

Row 4 (ws): Second strap: work in pattern to last 3 sts, k1, m1, p2. First strap: p2, m1, k1, work in pattern to end.

Work these four rows 3 (3, 3, 4, 4, 4) times.
24 (24, 24, 32, 32, 32) sts increased total.
30 (34, 38, 46, 50, 54) sts each side.

On the next rs row, work in pattern (no increases) to end of first strap.
Using knitted cast on, CO 22 (22, 30, 26, 32, 34) sts.
Work in pattern over second shoulder strap.
84 (90, 106, 118, 132, 142) sts total after all increases and neck CO. Shoulder straps connected.

Work in 2x2 rib. When piece measures 7 (7½, 9, 9½, 11, 11½)" from beginning, begin increasing for arm hole as follows:
Row 1 (rs): k1, m1, k1, work in pattern to last st, m1, k1.
Row 2 and all ws rows: knit the knits and purl the purls.
Row 3: k1, m1, work in pattern to last st, m1, k1.
Row 5: k2, m1pwise, work in pattern to last 2 sts, m1pwise, k2.
Row 7: k2, m1pwise, p1, work in pattern to last 3 sts, p1, m1pwise, k2.

Work these eight rows 2½ (2½, 2½, 3, 3, 3) times.
20 (20, 20, 24, 24, 24) sts increased. (Size 32, 36 and 40 will begin and end with k4 from now on. This will not be noticeable after seaming.)

After all increases, 102 (108, 126, 142, 156, 166) sts total.
Work in 2x2 rib until piece measures 18 (20, 22, 24, 26, 28)" from beginning.
BO all sts.

FINISHING:
Seam shoulders and side seams. Weave in all ends. Block, being careful not to stretch ribbing.

Charts

Strap One

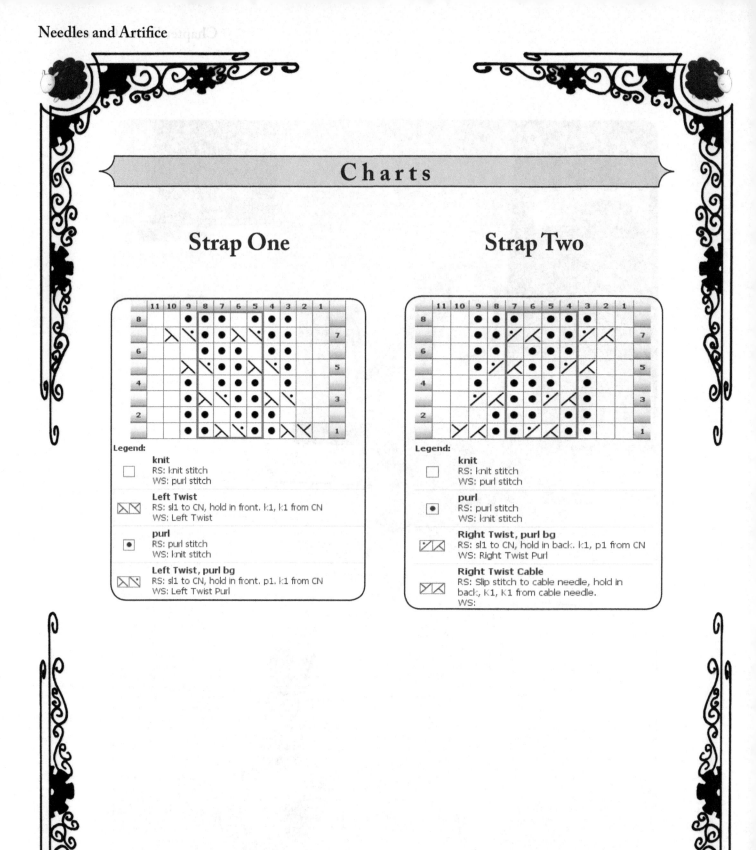

Legend:

	knit
□	RS: knit stitch
	WS: purl stitch

	Left Twist
◪	RS: sl1 to CN, hold in front. k1, k1 from CN
	WS: Left Twist

	purl
⊡	RS: purl stitch
	WS: knit stitch

	Left Twist, purl bg
◪	RS: sl1 to CN, hold in front. p1. k1 from CN
	WS: Left Twist Purl

Strap Two

Legend:

	knit
□	RS: knit stitch
	WS: purl stitch

	purl
⊡	RS: purl stitch
	WS: knit stitch

	Right Twist, purl bg
◪	RS: sl1 to CN, hold in back. k1, p1 from CN
	WS: Right Twist Purl

	Right Twist Cable
◪	RS: Slip stitch to cable needle, hold in back, k1, k1 from cable needle.
	WS:

Vest Body

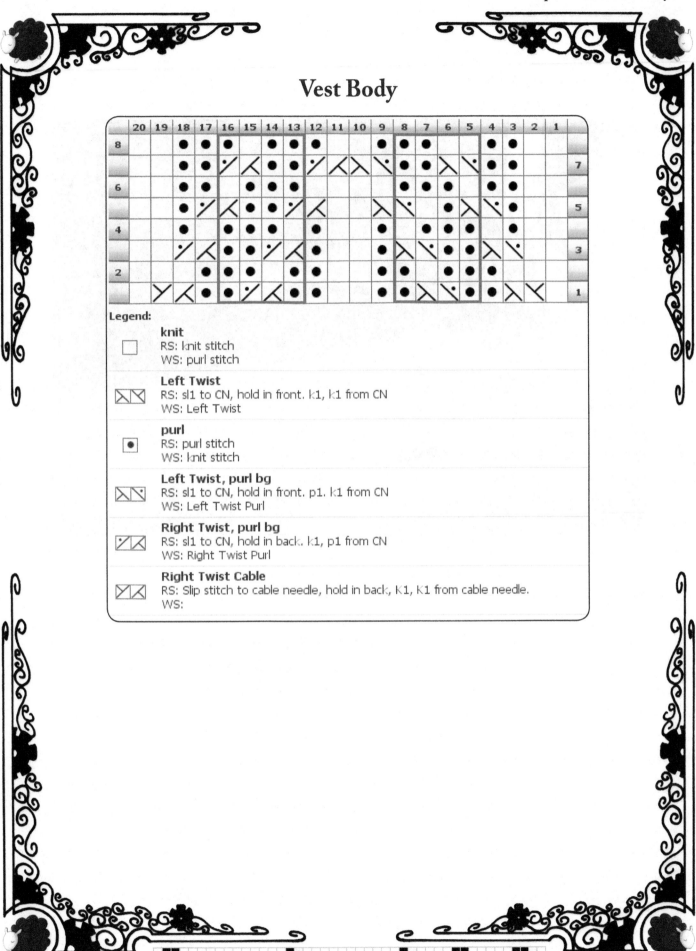

Legend:

	knit
☐	RS: knit stitch
	WS: purl stitch

	Left Twist
◩◪	RS: sl1 to CN, hold in front. k1, k1 from CN
	WS: Left Twist

	purl
⊡	RS: purl stitch
	WS: knit stitch

	Left Twist, purl bg
◩◪	RS: sl1 to CN, hold in front. p1. k1 from CN
	WS: Left Twist Purl

	Right Twist, purl bg
◪◩	RS: sl1 to CN, hold in back. k1, p1 from CN
	WS: Right Twist Purl

	Right Twist Cable
◪◩	RS: Slip stitch to cable needle, hold in back, K1, K1 from cable needle.
	WS:

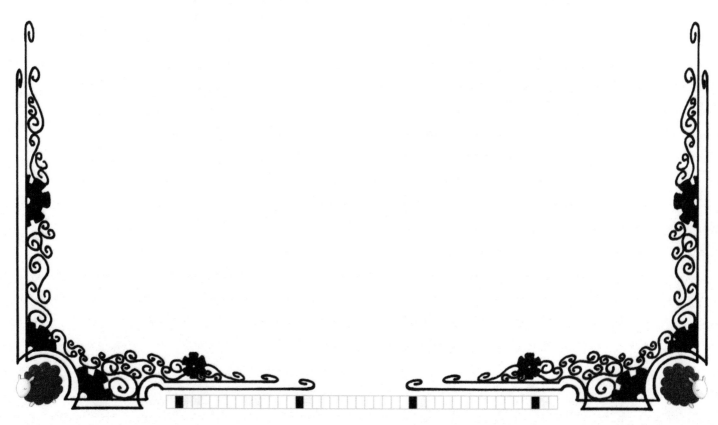

The Take Flight Bonnet

By: Jen Schripsema

DESCRIPTION:
Bottom up aviator-style hat worked flat to form the brim and then joined in the round. Slipped stitches form a herringbone pattern that looks great in a yarn with crisp stitch definition.

FINISHED DIMENSIONS:
Head circumference: 21"

YARN AND YARDAGE:
Alpine by JulieSpins, http://www.artfire.com/ext/shop/studio/JulieSpins
100% superwash merino; 270yds (247m) per 100g; DK weight
Color: Alpine, 2 skeins

GAUGE:
Knitted and blocked gauge:
In stockinette: 22 sts x 24 rows = 4"/10cm
In pattern: 26 sts x 56 rows = 4"/10cm

Despite the idyllic beauty of the Tingley ranch, eventually the mountain breezes call once again and ignite the need for adventure. Although designed for protection while up in the clouds, wherever your journey takes you, this charming bonnet is sure to suit any excursion!

NEEDLES AND NOTIONS:
32" size 5 US/3.75mm circular needle
-OR- one set size 5 US/3.75mm straight needles and one set size 5 US/3.75mm dpns (the bonnet is knit flat to start and finished in the round).
Crochet hook
Two ¾" D-rings
Tapestry needle

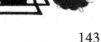

Pattern

CO 130 sts.
Purl one row.
To work the first row of the chart, slip 1, repeat Row 1 of the chart four times, then knit the last stitch.
Continue working back and forth from the chart, slipping the first stitch and knitting the last stitch of each row on rs rows and purling the last stitch on ws rows. Remember when working ws rows that you must purl and slip the stitches with the yarn held behind.

Repeat rows 1-16 four times. Total rows: 65

Work Row 17 of the chart to 1 stitch from the end. Pm, then knit the last stitch together with the first stitch of the next row to join in the round, pm. The stitch between these two markers marks the beginning of the round and should be knit each row.

Work Row 18 of the chart, placing markers as follows:

Work 16 sts, pm, *work 32 sts, pm,* repeat between * 2 more times for a total number of 3 repeats, work 16 sts, sm, k1, sm. The four new markers indicate the decrease points.
Continue knitting from the chart, decreasing every other row.

When you reach the end of the chart, break yarn and thread it through the remaining 9 stitches to gather. Weave in the ends.

Straps:
Pick up and knit 5 stitches from the selvedge edge, at the bottom front corners at either side of the hat.

Knit in garter stitch, slipping the first stitch of each row until straps measure 3 inches slightly stretched.

Bind off.

CHART NOTES:

The stitches in the chart represent one quarter of the total stitches in each row; you will knit each section four times per row.

Rows 1-16 of the chart are knit flat and repeated 4 times (for a total of 65 rows, including the inital purl row); thereafter, the work is joined and knit in the round.

The red border indicates the repeat for the herringbone stitch pattern.

FINISHING:

Weave in ends.

Starting at the back join, add a single crochet border all around the edge.

Slip both D-rings onto one strap. Fold the strap up just enough to form a channel for the D-rings. Sew the end down.

Wet block.

Chart

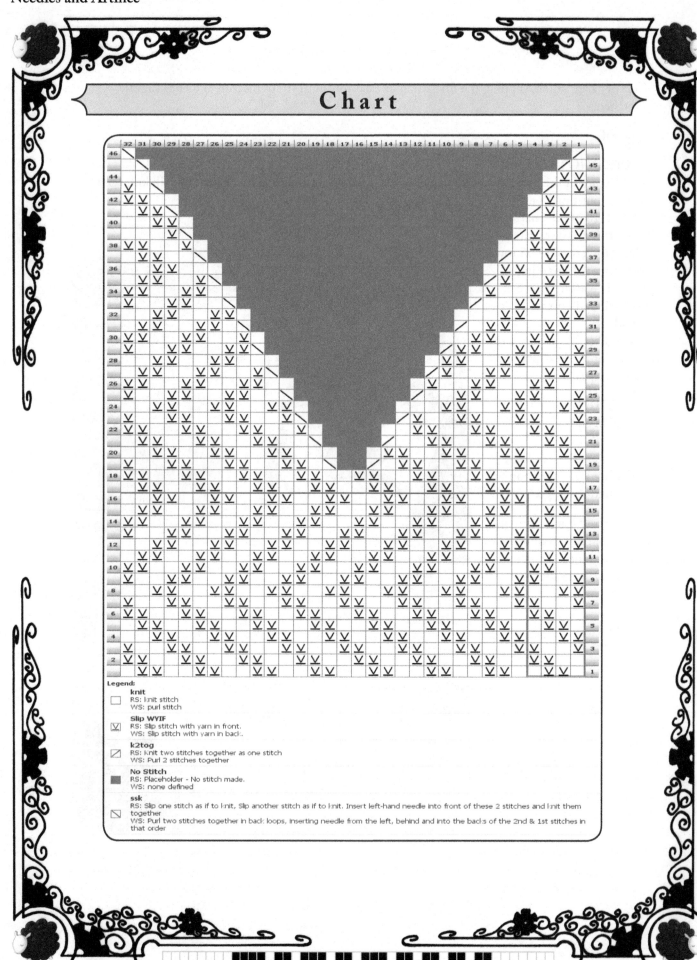

Legend:

knit
RS: knit stitch
WS: purl stitch

Slip WYIF
RS: Slip stitch with yarn in front.
WS: Slip stitch with yarn in back.

k2tog
RS: Knit two stitches together as one stitch
WS: Purl 2 stitches together

No Stitch
RS: Placeholder - No stitch made.
WS: none defined

ssk
RS: Slip one stitch as if to knit, Slip another stitch as if to knit. Insert left-hand needle into front of these 2 stitches and knit them together
WS: Purl two stitches together in back loops, inserting needle from the left, behind and into the backs of the 2nd & 1st stitches in that order

Chapter Five

In which there is shouting and snogging

Dr. Erma Melanogaster was adjusting the speed of her Mechanized Floral Vivification Machine when her brooch chimed. The engine was terribly loud, so she only noticed a flashing light on one of the gears deep in the machine. She moved, and it disappeared. She spent several minutes trying to track down the mysteriously moving light before passing in front of a greenhouse glass panel and discovering it in her own reflection. The brooch stopped flashing as she watched, so she shrugged and went back to work. It seemed like only moments later when she was interrupted by a message from Coraline. She hastily scrawled a response, and was about to continue her work when the meaning of the message truly sank in. The Ladies needed her help, and to perform her duty she had to do something she hadn't done in years: shop for a new ballgown.

****

Mrs. Theodosia LaDuke was an irrepressible seafaring Lady. As a child, her explorer's soul always yearned for wide open ocean and exotic vistas. Her family was terribly proper and disapproving of her ambitions, and for many years she lived a landlocked life. Her passion lead her to study celestial navigation and the accounts of distant lands written by anthropologists. She was determined to explore the oceans and visit all the continents, but could not leave her family until her father's death. Theodosia's route to adventure was not easy, and had to be won through cleverness and iron-willed endurance. Her father's estate was passed to Mr. Beechwood, a distant cousin with the required masculine characteristics. Theodosia did not dismay, for she had an ingenious plan. Mr. Beechwood was a deeply odious man, his one grace being that he was easy to charm. Within days of the funeral he and Theodosia were married. After that, it was only a small bit of work to secure a loan for half the inheritance, commission the tall ship Coriolis, and sail away to explore the Amazon Basin. Her husband was surprised upon waking to discover a note wishing him well in his life without her.

Kristoff paced back and forth through the increasingly-crowded confines of the airship bridge. It required quite a lot of skill to do so without crumpling a skirt, kicking a ball of yarn, or tripping over a small sheep, but he'd had considerable practice by this point. As he completed his pacing circuit he fought the urge to ask how much longer it would take to get to London.

"Five minutes less than it took when you asked five minutes ago," Anna chirped from her perch on a bookshelf, the chestnut sheep nestled in her lap. She had named the sheep Arcadibaa, which had caused a groan of epic proportions to go round the bridge.

Kristoff paused and attempted to glower at her. He wasn't very good at it. "I didn't actually ask."

"No, but you were clearly thinking it. I could even tell it from here!" Peter said. He was seated on the floor, tinkering with a device on the bridge wall, which intermittently produced deep rumbling sounds followed by a strange mechanical bleat. "Aha!" He twisted

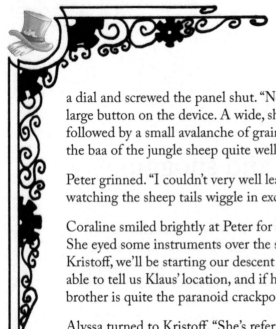

a dial and screwed the panel shut. "Now let's see if it works!" He winked at Coraline and pushed a large button on the device. A wide, shallow tray popped out of the wall, and the rumbling sound was followed by a small avalanche of grain, filling the trough. The mechanical bleat sounded, mimicking the baa of the jungle sheep quite well. They all crowded over and started munching grain.

Peter grinned. "I couldn't very well leave them out while we enjoy our tea!" The Ladies all laughed, watching the sheep tails wiggle in excitement.

Coraline smiled brightly at Peter for a moment, then straightened her face and turned back to work. She eyed some instruments over the shoulder of a crew-member and stood up with a nod. "Cheer up, Kristoff, we'll be starting our descent soon. We will meet with Erma just outside of London. She'll be able to tell us Klaus' location, and if he's at his estate, we'll need her knowledge to get in safely. Your brother is quite the paranoid crackpot. I've heard his security systems are...unusual."

Alyssa turned to Kristoff. "She's referring to Dr. Erma Melanogaster. She's a smashing scientist and also quite a beauty, though she is sadly unaware of it most of the time." Alyssa sighed as if this was the darkest tragedy. "She worked for Klaus for a while, until she realized where his plans were leading. She's the one that contacted me about the plot before you two arrived at my door in Shanghai."

"How could anyone work with Klaus? Especially one of you Ladies?" Kristoff was indignant.

"Well, dear Erma has always been fascinated by the details of scientific discovery. Which is a passion I share, of course." Caldonia smiled slightly, and the crewman attending her smiled quickly in response. "But she has a tendency to go...deep into her work. She doesn't always see the bigger picture or the danger, if she has an interesting problem to puzzle through. And she became much more daring after the accident."

Kristoff raised an eyebrow. When no one continued, he cleared his throat quietly. The Ladies kept sipping tea and knitting. The sheep kept munching. How could everyone stay so quiet now, when the most intriguing conversation topic had just been raised? Finally, he gave in. "What accident?"

Anna, who had been watching his increasing discomfort with amusement, leaped to her feet and gestured grandly. "It was a dark and stormy night..." she began.

Kristoff rolled his eyes. "And it was a storm like no other, of course."

Anna grinned. His fledgling sarcasm was quite adorable. She continued, "All right, it was a regular day. Erma was working on some sort of timekeeping device--"

"It was a clockwork timer for her greenhouse!" Theodosia chimed in. "She was connecting it all together when BOOM!"

Anna frowned briefly at Theodosia and picked the story back up. "She looked away for a minute, BOOM!, then she woke up on the floor of her lab, somewhat exploded."

"How can you be somewhat exploded?" Kristoff scoffed.

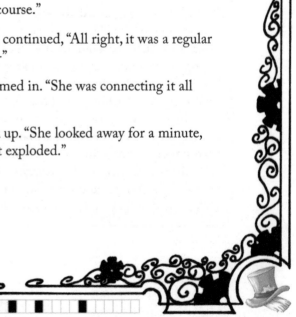

"Oh, she does it all the time. Her experiment blows up, she ends up deaf for a while and covered in soot, but still alive. She really should consider coming to my ranch to do her experiments, it's a much safer environment." Miriam sipped her tea, already a touch homesick.

Alyssa brightened, "Coraline, do you remember that time she showed up at the Fethiway's garden party after being exploded?"

Coraline laughed merrily. "Yes, she was so deaf we had to write questions to her in jam on the toast!" She leaned back into Peter, who was following the tale with rapt attention.

"So if she gets 'exploded' all the time, why was this one day different?" Kristoff frequently found the wandering conversations of the Ladies a bit maddening.

"Ah, well that day she was more than just exploded. She found a gash on her jaw, just here." Caldonia pointed to a spot slightly south of her ear. "And then when she examined herself with one of her dreadfully dangerous machines, she discovered a...new addition."

"Ooh! Let me tell this part!" Theodosia bounced in her seat, dislodging her knitting entirely. Peter smoothly picked it up and offered it back to her. She nodded quickly at him and continued. "When she scanned herself, she found a strange object lodged in her brain! No, really! The timer she was working on when things exploded just slipped right in! It's a wonder that she managed to survive at all! And when it goes off, she goes a little mad!"

Alyssa winced at this description. "Mad isn't the right word at all. She just gets a bit more...impulsive. Emotional. Excitable. It makes her forget about her own safety. And, sometimes she has significant breakthroughs while in that state, so it can actually be quite beneficial."

Kristoff shook his head. He wasn't entirely sure if the Ladies were playing a joke on him, but it did make sense. Only a mad person would work with Klaus for long.

"Don't think of her as impaired by this." Coraline spoke sternly to Kristoff. "She still has excellent manners and manages quite well in society. In fact, she's at a ball tonight, which is where we'll pick her up." Coraline paused for a moment, then forged ahead. "The ball is at your family's estate, Kristoff. When I heard about the crash, I worried that Klaus might try to accelerate his plans and impersonate you at the ball. Erma is investigating, and she will let us know when we arrive whether Klaus is there. If he didn't show, we'll pick Erma up and head straight to his estate."

There was a short moment of silence.

"No." Kristoff's voice had a newfound weight to it.

Alyssa sat up in her chaise. "No? Haven't you been in an incredible hurry to get to Klaus since before we left?" The rest of the Ladies on the bridge echoed this statement, some a bit more grumpily than others.

"Yes. But there's something that I have to do first." He turned and regarded the Ladies of Mischief, face tense with anger. "This entire stupid enterprise is the fault of two people."

A collective breath was held around the bridge.

Kristoff smiled a tight, angry smile. "I need to speak to my parents."

"Lovely! I'll change into my party dress!" Alyssa was positively giddy at the prospect of attending a ball.

"And I'll make sure I have my party gun!" Anna chimed in. Everyone turned to look at her, and she frowned. "What?"

Miriam finally broke the silence. "Do you actually have a gun especially for parties, or is that just a figure of speech?"

Anna laughed. "Sometimes, if my guns are very good, they get to go pretty places with me."

"They'll have a chance soon enough," Coraline interjected. "We're making our descent."

****

The doorman looked over the motley crew before him. Most of them were women (he couldn't bring himself to call them ladies, though several of them were quite well-dressed) with the one man standing slightly in front. He caught a glimpse of something he thought might be a sheep; whatever it was, it was certainly not allowed inside.

"I'm sorry, but if Sir wishes to enter Sir will need an invitation," he droned. "The Lord and Lady of the house are entertaining tonight and as such are not available to see..." There was a significant pause as he looked over the group again. "Those such as yourselves," he finally finished.

"Get out of our way, you thrice-frogged idiot," Anna snarled. "Don't you recognize Kristoff?" She strode forward, mayhem on her mind, and Kristoff tossed out an arm to stop her.

"Anna. This is my house. Allow me to handle this, please?" He looked her in the eyes for a moment, and she sighed and stepped back, grumbling. Kristoff smiled at her. "Thank you, Anna." He patted her on the shoulder and turned back to the doorman.

The next thing anyone knew, the doorman was laid flat out on the ground and Kristoff was rubbing his right knuckles with his left hand. "I never really liked him," Kristoff said to the world at large. "He was always too damned proper."

Anna looked from Kristoff to the doorman and back, blinking. She shook her head sharply. "Right. Onward to your parents, then?" He nodded and led the Ladies inside. Kristoff had to admit it felt quite nice to have a small army backing him up for this. It was a conversation that was a long time coming. Down this hall,

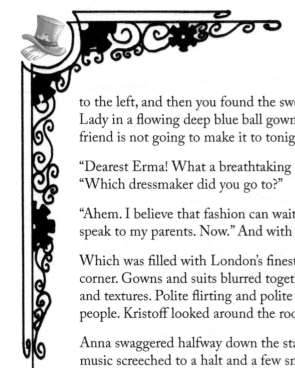

to the left, and then you found the sweeping staircase into the ballroom. As they reached the stairs a Lady in a flowing deep blue ball gown stepped out from the nearby shadows. "Ladies! It appears our friend is not going to make it to tonight's ball." She winked at Coraline.

"Dearest Erma! What a breathtaking gown!" Alyssa was completely distracted from the mission. "Which dressmaker did you go to?"

"Ahem. I believe that fashion can wait." Kristoff watched as disbelief passed over Alyssa's face. "I must speak to my parents. Now." And with that, he strode into the ballroom.

Which was filled with London's finest, waltzing to the strains of the string quartet playing in the corner. Gowns and suits blurred together to fill the room with a constantly changing tableau of colors and textures. Polite flirting and polite arguing went on everywhere, sometimes between the same people. Kristoff looked around the room for his parents, debating the best way to go about this.

Anna swaggered halfway down the staircase, paused, and casually fired her rifle into the air. The music screeched to a halt and a few small screams could be heard as the guests milled about in confusion. Anna beamed as all eyes came to rest on her.

"Right, then," she called cheerfully into the silence. "Are the Lord and Lady Von Boltenstein at home? Only there's someone here who wants to talk to them." She started down the stairs as Kristoff and the other Ladies followed her. The guests slowly pulled back from the base of the stairs, leaving an open space in the center of the room for the intruders. As they passed a servant holding a tray of hor d'ourves, Anna snatched up a tart and flung it directly into the face of a man on the other side of the circle. He staggered for a moment and took his hand out of his jacket. Anna wagged her finger at him. "Going for your pistol? Foolish man. I'm not here to shoot anyone unless they shoot at me first. Now, where are the Lord and Lady Von Boltenstein?"

"You impertinent slattern!" The Lady Von Boltenstein swept out to meet Anna and the Ladies, followed closely by her husband. Her face was contorted with rage. "How dare you insult my house and my family with your presence? After what you did the last time?" The Lord Von Boltenstein was content to simply glare at Anna, allowing his wife to do all the insulting.

Anna smirked. "Seems to me it's not your whole family that finds my presence an insult... Wouldn't you say, Kristoff?" With a dramatic gesture of her hand, she stepped aside.

Kristoff strode forward, radiating anger, and his mother actually took a step back as he glared at her. "Kristoff?! You're all right! When you were kidnapped, we thought--"

"Oh, stuff it, Mother." Kristoff snapped. "You know perfectly well I wasn't kidnapped. You were there."

"Yes, we were there when this... This, commoner took you away on her horse. After destroying your engagement party, no less!" Kristoff's mother spoke slightly more loudly than was required, and even turned slightly away from Kristoff to make sure the guests heard her.

"I went willingly, Mother, and I never wanted to marry Elaine to begin with. That's not why I'm here." Kristoff fixed his parents with an icy stare. "I'm here because you are both complete blooming idiots, and because of that, Klaus is trying to kill me."

"What? Klaus?!" The Lady Von Boltenstein gasped. "What does Klaus have to do with anything?"

Kristoff rolled his eyes and snorted. "Klaus has everything to do with this. You had to be so traditional! I was the older one, so I therefore had to inherit everything! I got all the best schools, the best clothes, the best training to take over your stupid estate! Klaus got nothing! You shipped him out to the country where he wouldn't cause any trouble and then just ignored him. Now he intends to kill me and take my place in Society, which would be child's play because most of the people in this room don't even know you have two twin sons!" He shouted the last bit, just to make sure everyone heard.

"Kristoff! You're going to cause a scandal!" the Lady hissed at him, motioning him to keep it down. Kristoff laughed loudly. "Oh, Mother! You and your ridiculous scandals. So afraid of causing one, yet loving it so much whenever one befell our neighbors. You want a scandal? I can give one to you."

Kristoff turned to Anna and grabbed her rifle before tossing it to a convenient Coraline. Before Coraline had even caught the gun, he'd pulled Anna into a firm embrace and was kissing her like both their lives depended on it. Tittering, gasps, and applause from the Ladies could be heard around the ballroom. Miriam pulled out her pocket-watch and timed the two of them, looking impressed.

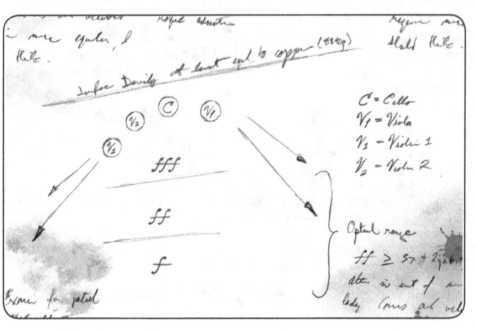

When they surfaced for air some time later, the Lady Von Boltenstein looked like she'd swallowed a live spider that was trying to fight its way back up her throat. She sniffed and looked away. "Yes, Kristoff, many men hire harlots. Most don't do it in front of their mothers."

"Harlot?!" Kristoff nearly leaped at his mother, and Anna only just managed to hold him back. "She's not a harlot, Mother! She's the woman I love and am damn well going to marry!" He paused, replayed the last sentence in his head and swallowed. He turned to the extremely perplexed redhead. "That is, if you want to, Anna?"

Anna laughed and wrapped her arm around his waist. "Of course, darling. But you really have terrible timing." She stood on her tiptoes to give him a small kiss and bounced back down to her heels. "Now, then. You should wrap this up. We have to go beat the stuffing out of your brother."

Kristoff turned back to his parents, finding himself grinning like a loon. There was really no way not to look like that at the moment. He looked his parents up and down. His mother was horrified. His father looked... Proud? He met the older Boltenstein's eyes and his father winked at him. Kristoff sniggered. No wonder the man almost never spoke.

"Now, then, Mother. I'm going to go clean up your mess, and take care of Klaus. And you know what the stupidest thing is?"

His mother shook her head.

"If you'd ever just once asked us, I'd have told you to let Klaus inherit everything. I never wanted this life. I never wanted all the responsibility you forced on me. You're the one who decided I should have it, and you're the one whose fault this is." Kristoff met her eyes. "I'm going to leave with Anna, and the life I have with her is a thousand times happier than the one you were building for me. If you can't accept that, you're not welcome at our wedding." Leaving those words hanging in the air, he turned on his heel and strode out of the ballroom, Anna by his side.

As the Ladies of Mischief trailed out after them (Erma had to jog to catch up, having become distracted by the play of light across the crystal chandelier, and then with filling her purse with plundered pastries), Theodosia was fairly skipping with glee. "Do you know, I think that was the very finest party I've ever attended? I think I even saw the Prime Minister!"

Alyssa pondered for a moment, then shook her head. "It was quite nice, but I've seen better."

"Oh?" Theodosia's face begged for more information.

Alyssa nodded. "Well, I've been to finer parties for sure, but I expected this one to be more fun. You see, I was really hoping that Anna would punch someone. Whenever Anna gets to punch someone, the parties improve immeasurably." She paused. "But don't anyone tell her I said so."

"Too late!" Anna's voice carried back down the hall, and the Ladies burst into laughter. As they giggled, Anna pulled Kristoff close and leaned her head into his shoulder. "Now to face Klaus, yeah?"

Kristoff looked down at her and was shocked to see worry on her face. "Yes. What's wrong?"

Anna shook her head. "Nothing. Just... Be careful when we go in there. He wants us dead, and..." She sighed. "I don't want to lose you. I love you."

Kristoff smiled. "I love you, too, Anna."

"Time to kick your brother's arse?"

"Indeed."

The Quadrille Overbust Corset

By: Valerie DiPietro

DESCRIPTION:

This knit corset is intended to be worn on top of a fully cinched and boned 15 inch overbust corset. We would recommend the Simplicity pattern 9769 if you are sewing your own, or a comparably shaped commercial corset of your choice. You may choose to knit it as a bodice style top but make sure to mind the waist measurements and make adjustments as necessary since it is intended to fall on a cinched waist.

To choose your size put on the corset of your choice cinched down and choose the pattern measurement that corresponds to your largest measurement. While a corset is made or purchased based on the waist measurement this knit garment is designed for the easiest alteration based on the largest measurement of the three. Three points of

Society functions are rife with twists and turns, gay music and dizzying conversation. But you will never miss a step in this lyrical creation worn over a traditional corset, which uses the weaving cables to make partners of shape and texture. Prepare yourself for a full dance card, and be sure to stop and catch your breath!

reference are given: hip, waist, and full bust. These three points will then be adjusted to fit your actual measurements.

The corset is knit flat from the bottom up in reverse stockinette. Boning channels and lacing are added to the back edges. The top of the corset has an eyelet finish with a picot bind off.

SPECIAL TECHNIQUES:
Picot Edge, Cabling

FINISHED DIMENSIONS:
Fitted over a cinched corset:
Full bust: 34 (38, 42, 44, 46)"
Waist: 23 (27, 31, 35, 39)"
Hip: 36 (40, 44, 48, 52)"
Length: 16"

TO FIT BODY MEASUREMENT:
Without corset:
Full bust: 34 (38, 42, 44, 46)"
Waist: 26 (30, 34, 38, 42)"
Hip: 36 (40, 44, 48, 52)"

EASE:
Negative ease, adjustable

YARN AND YARDAGE:
Super DK by Skein Yarns, http://skeinyarns.etsy.com
100% superwash merino; 230yds (210m) per 100g; DK weight
Color: Wintertide, 3 (3, 4, 4, 5, 5) skeins

GAUGE:
Ball band gauge of chosen yarn: 21-24 sts = 4"

Knitted and blocked gauge on Large needles (US 6):
In stockinette: 24 sts x 32 rows = 4"/10cm
In seed stitch: 24 sts x 36 rows = 4"/10cm

NEEDLES AND NOTIONS:
40" size 6 US/4.0mm circular needle
40" size 5 US/3.5mm circular needle
3-4 yds of ribbon for eyelet edge

6-8 yds of ribbon for back lacing

Two pieces ¼" steel or plastic corset boning, 15" long (or final length of finished back)

PATTERN NOTES:

This pattern is designed to fit over a corset that reduces your natural waist by 3 inches. If you are cinching tighter or looser than this please adjust accordingly. Also remember that with any corset this piece is not intended to close completely but rather has a gap in the back to show off lacing.

Throughout the pattern there will be many places at which adjustments can be made to fit your specific corset or body shape. Alterations will be very simple to do as long as you have measurements in inches for your specific shape. Be sure to try on your piece frequently and alter as necessary.

When altering the shape be very mindful of the center cable pattern. Altering the number of rows will change the row you will be ending this cable on when you reach the top of the piece.

Pattern

Cast on 200 (226, 250, 274, 298) stitches on smaller needle.

Row 1: k2, p1, k2 to establish edge. Begin working 2x2 rib until 5 stitches from end. K2, p1, k2.
Row 2: p2, k1, p2, work 2x2 rib until 5 stitches from end, p2, k1, p2.

Repeat these two rows for 1 inch ending after wrong side row.

Cable Set-Up Row:
Switch to larger needles. Begin with a right side row.

K2, p1, k2, pm, work Row 1 of Lacing Chart (14sts), pm, p6 (10, 14, 16, 18), pm, work Row 1 of Right Channel Chart (4sts), pm, p12 (14, 17, 20, 22), pm, work Row 1 of Right Channel Chart, pm, work in seed stitch for 18 (23, 25, 29, 35) stitches, pm, work Row 1 of Right Channel Chart, pm, p12 (14, 17, 20, 22), pm, work Row 1 of Right Channel Chart, pm, work Row 1 of Center Cable Chart (34sts), pm, work row 1 of Left Channel Chart (4sts), pm, p12 (14, 17, 20, 22), pm, work Row 1 of Left Channel Chart, pm, work in seed stitch for 18 (23, 25, 29, 35) stitches, pm, work Row 1 of Left Channel Chart, pm, p12 (14, 17, 20, 22), pm, work Row 1 of Left Channel Chart, pm, p6 (10, 14, 16, 18), pm, work Row 1 of Lacing Chart (14sts), pm, k2, p1, k2.

Next row and all wrong side rows: p2, k1, p2, work in pattern as appropriate maintaining cables until 5 stitches from the end, p2, k1, p2.

Next row and all right side rows: k2, p1, k2, work in pattern as appropriate maintaining cables until 5 stitches from the end, k2, p1, k2.
Work in pattern as established for 8 rows or 1 inch.

Begin Decreases for Waist Shaping:
NOTE: At this point if you would like to obtain a longer distance from hip to waist simply knit more plain rows between decrease rows. To obtain either a smaller waist line or a larger waist line adjust the number of stitches decreased to accommodate your measurements so the measurement

given at the end of the decrease section matches your desired waist measurement.

Right side row: work in pattern decreasing one stitch before and after (p2tog before and ssp after) each Channel Chart except for those flanking the Center Cable Chart; decrease on the far side of those channels only, not inside the Center Chart. 14 sts decreased.

Work in pattern for 3 rows.

Repeat these four rows another 4 times for a total of 20 rows.

Work to 2 stitches before first channel. P2tog, work across to the channel before the seed stitch panel. Work channel, sm, p2tog, work until 2 stitches before marker, ssp, work channel chart. Mirror for second half of the row. 6 sts decreased.

Work in pattern for 3 rows.

Repeat these four rows 0 (2, 2, 2, 2) more times, for a total of 4 (12, 12, 12, 12) rows.

Work next four rows twice for all sizes except smallest.

Row 1: work in pattern, decreasing one stitch before first Cable Channel and after last Cable Channel. 2 sts decreased.
Rows 2-4: work in pattern as established.

Work straight in pattern until the piece measures 6 inches long from the cast on edge, ending after a ws row. This is your smallest waist measurement plus two inches for selvedge.
Total stitches: 130 (134, 158, 182, 206)

Work in pattern for 8 rows.

Begin Increases for Bust:
First Bust Increase Set:
Work in pattern for 8 rows.

Work in pattern, increasing one stitch (m1p) before and after each Channel Chart except for inside Center Cable section.

Work in pattern for 3 rows. Work in pattern until marker indicating the start of seed stitch panel. Slip marker, m1r, work to marker, m1l, slip marker, work in pattern to end.

Work in pattern for 19 rows, ending with a ws row.

Second Bust Increase Set:
rs row: work in pattern increasing one stitch before and after each Channel Chart except for Center Cable Chart.

Work in pattern for 7 rows. Repeat these 8 rows 2 more times.

Work to first Channel Chart, m1p before working chart, work all the way through seed stitch panel and Channel Chart, sm, m1p, work to marker, m1p, sm, work Center Chart and Channel Chart, sm, m1p, work to marker, m1p, work through last channel chart, m1p, work to end.

Work in pattern until the piece measures 36 (40, 44, 48, 52) inches across and 14 inches long from cast on edge. This is your bust measurement plus two inches for selvedge.
Total stitches: 208 (212, 236, 260, 284)

Work in pattern for 3 rows.

At this point end all cables but maintain selvedge edge.

rs row: K2, p1, k2, *p3, yo, p2tog,* repeat between * until 5 stitches from end, k2, p1, k2.

Work two rows in reverse stockinette, maintaining edge pattern but not cables.

Bind off loosely with picot: CO 2 stitches, BO 4 stitches, repeat across row.

FINISHING:

At back edges, fold over vertically at purl row and stitch down to create boning channel. Stitch boning channel closed at bottom to form a pocket. Insert boning into pockets and stitch top shut.

Block finished corset paying particular attention to the picot bind off.

Stitch end of ribbon to the upper back on the inside of the piece (near top of boning channel), then thread through yarn overs until you reach the center. Do this on both sides so you can tie the ribbon at the front. This allows you to cinch the top over your breasts. Wear the bow outside, or tucked in.

Use ribbon or lacing of your choice to lace the corset through eyelets down back of piece within the back Lacing Cables.

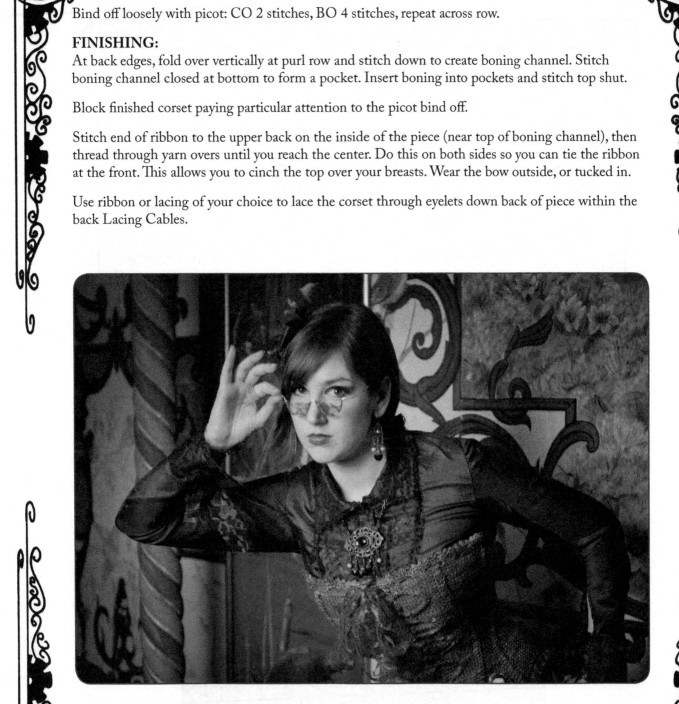

Charts

Right Channel

	4	3	2	1	
2					
					1

Legend:

c2 over 2 left
RS: sl 2 to CN, hold in front. k2, k2 from CN
WS: none defined

knit
RS: knit stitch
WS: purl stitch

Left Channel

	4	3	2	1	
2					
					1

Legend:

c2 over 2 right
RS: sl2 to CN, hold in back. k2, k2 from CN
WS: none defined

knit
RS: knit stitch
WS: purl stitch

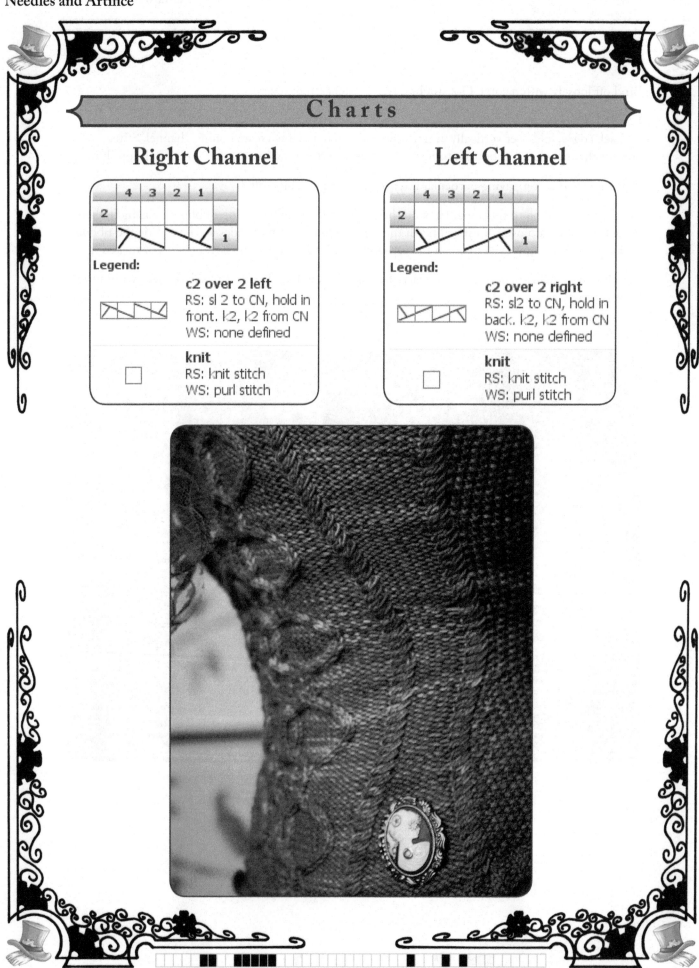

Lacing Cable

	14	13	12	11	10	9	8	7	6	5	4	3	2	1	
8	●	B	●				B					●	B	●	
	●	B	●			\	O	O	/			●	B	●	7
6	●	B	●									●	B	●	
	●	B	●	\			V		/			●	B	●	5
4	●	B	●				B					●	B	●	
	●	B	●			\	O	O	/			●	B	●	3
2	●	B	●									●	B	●	
	●	B	●	\			V		/			●	B	●	1

Legend:

purl
RS: purl stitch
WS: knit stitch

knit tbl
RS: Knit stitch through back loop
WS: Purl stitch through back loop

c2 over 2 left
RS: sl 2 to CN, hold in front. k2, k2 from CN
WS: none defined

c2 over 2 right
RS: sl2 to CN, hold in back. k2, k2 from CN
WS: none defined

knit
RS: knit stitch
WS: purl stitch

k2tog
RS: Knit two stitches together as one stitch
WS: Purl 2 stitches together

yo
RS: Yarn Over
WS: Yarn Over

ssk
RS: Slip one stitch as if to knit, Slip another stitch as if to knit. Insert left-hand needle into front of these 2 stitches and knit them together
WS: Purl two stitches together in back loops, inserting needle from the left, behind and into the backs of the 2nd & 1st stitches in that order

Center Cable (rotated clockwise)

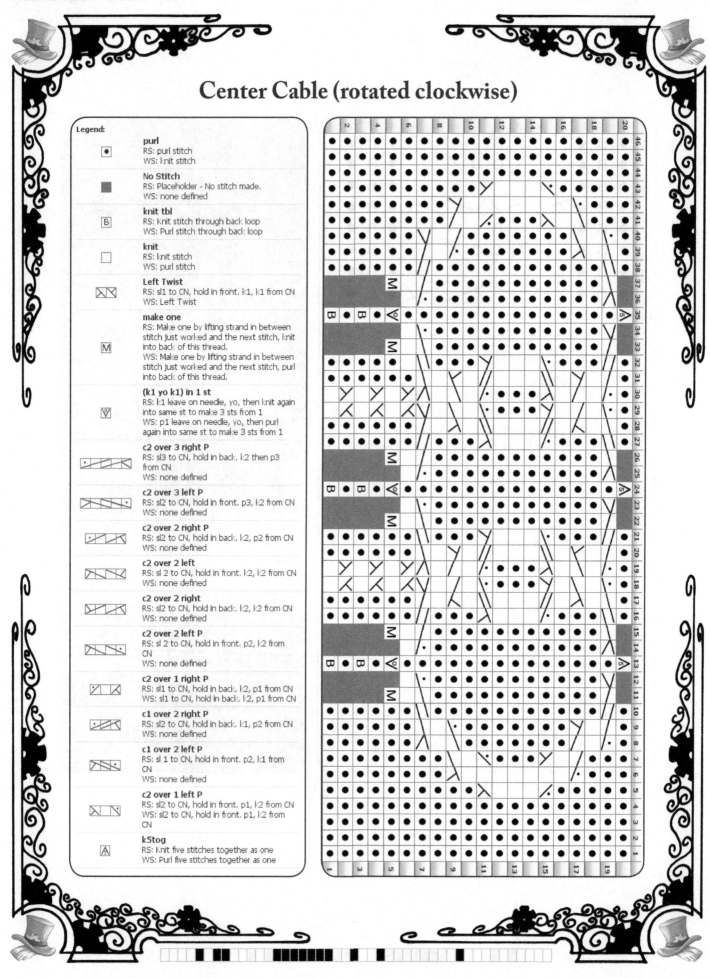

Legend:

⊙	**purl**	RS: purl stitch WS: knit stitch
■	**No Stitch**	RS: Placeholder - No stitch made. WS: none defined
B	**knit tbl**	RS: Knit stitch through back loop WS: Purl stitch through back loop
□	**knit**	RS: knit stitch WS: purl stitch
⧅	**Left Twist**	RS: sl1 to CN, hold in front. k1, k1 from CN WS: Left Twist
M	**make one**	RS: Make one by lifting strand in between stitch just worked and the next stitch, knit into back of this thread. WS: Make one by lifting strand in between stitch just worked and the next stitch, purl into back of this thread.
V	**(k1 yo k1) in 1 st**	RS: k1 leave on needle, yo, then knit again into same st to make 3 sts from 1 WS: p1 leave on needle, yo, then purl again into same st to make 3 sts from 1
	c2 over 3 right P	RS: sl3 to CN, hold in back. k2 then p3 from CN WS: none defined
	c2 over 3 left P	RS: sl2 to CN, hold in front. p3, k2 from CN WS: none defined
	c2 over 2 right P	RS: sl2 to CN, hold in back. k2, p2 from CN WS: none defined
	c2 over 2 left	RS: sl 2 to CN, hold in front. k2, k2 from CN WS: none defined
	c2 over 2 right	RS: sl2 to CN, hold in back. k2, k2 from CN WS: none defined
	c2 over 2 left P	RS: sl 2 to CN, hold in front. p2, k2 from CN WS: none defined
	c2 over 1 right P	RS: sl1 to CN, hold in back. k2, p1 from CN WS: sl1 to CN, hold in back. k2, p1 from CN
	c1 over 2 right P	RS: sl2 to CN, hold in back. k1, p2 from CN WS: none defined
	c1 over 2 left P	RS: sl 1 to CN, hold in front. p2, k1 from CN WS: none defined
	c2 over 1 left P	RS: sl2 to CN, hold in front. p1, k2 from CN WS: sl2 to CN, hold in front. p1, k2 from CN
A	**k5tog**	RS: Knit five stitches together as one WS: Purl five stitches together as one

The Cameo Spencer Jacket

By: Sarra Loew

DESCRIPTION:

Cropped sweater knit bottom up with set in puffed sleeves. Knit in one piece until armhole. Vertically rounded front opening with 5" of overlap. 2" ruffle picked up and added from right side up rounded front and around neck. Sleeve has chain detail running up center with decreases to the side helping create the volume in the sleeve. Sleeve has large puff shoulder.

Like a classic beauty carved in shell, you will be an elegant portrait in this stunning cropped piece, styled to frame your lovely face and figure, while highlighting your ensemble. Every detail is a masterpiece, from the ingenious sleeve shaping, to the playful ruffled edging. This garment truly showcases the work of art you are.

SPECIAL TECHNIQUES :

Chain Pattern (5 sts):

Row 1-3: p1, k3, p1

Row 4: p1, k1, yo, k1, place three stitches just worked back on left needle. Pass fourth stitch over the three completed stitches. Place the three stitches back on right needle. P1.

Repeat these four rows for the section worked in the round.

When you begin working flat, work Rows 2 and 4 as established on the rs of the piece, and work Rows 1 and 3 on the ws as follows: k1, p3, k1 to maintain the stockinette pattern on the right side of work.

Buttonhole Rows:

Row 1 (rs): (increase, k1, or decrease), k2, ssk, yo2, k2tog, work to end.

ws: work to buttonhole stitches, p2 (the k2tog and one yo), ptbl twice (the other yo and ssk).

FINISHED DIMENSIONS:

Underbust: 28 (30, 32, 34, 36, 38, 40, 42)"

Overbust: 31 (33, 35, 37, 39, 42, 44, 46)"

Wrist: 6 (6, 6½, 6½, 7, 7, 7½, 7¾)"

Bicep: 11 (11½, 12, 13, 13½, 14, 14½, 15)"

Body Length: 11"

TO FIT BODY MEASUREMENTS:

Underbust: 30 (32, 34, 36, 38, 40, 42, 44)" - Note that this should be measured over the clothing you plan to wear with the sweater.

Cup Sizes: A (B, C, D, E, F) Note that cup size is relative to the underbust measurement, which should be taken over clothes, so this measurement may not match your bra size. If your bust measurement is 1 inch larger than your underbust (in planned clothing), then use the A size instructions. Go up a letter for each additional inch difference between your bust and your underbust.

EASE:
2 inches negative ease in body. No ease in sleeve, except at puff sleeve top.

YARN AND YARDAGE:
Bacchus by Pigeonroof Studios,
http://pigeonroofstudios.etsy.com
60% Merino, 40% silk; 200 yds (183 m) per 100 g; Aran weight
Color: Oak, 6 (7, 7, 8, 9, 10, 10, 11) skeins

NOTE: Silk blends tend to grow during blocking. Make sure your gauge is for a blocked swatch.

GAUGE:
Ball band gauge of chosen yarn: 18 sts = 4"/10cm
Knitted and blocked gauge:
In stockinette: 21 sts x 30 rows = 4"/10cm

NEEDLES AND NOTIONS:
36" 5 US/3.75mm circular needle
12 buttons
Stitch markers
1 yd velvet ribbon for collar lining

PATTERN NOTES:
While working the body, you will be increasing along the right front edge, working buttonholes on the right front edge, increasing for vertical bust darts, adding bust shaping with short rows, and increasing along the side seams. The row counts restart after the hem fold. Read the instructions very carefully.

Pattern

Body:
Cast on 147 (158, 168, 179, 189, 200, 210, 221) stitches.
Knit 12 rows stockinette, ending with a ws row.
Folded hem: fold fabric and knit cast on stitches together with live stitches across. This makes a nice finished bottom hem.
Purl 1 row.

Vertical Bust Darts (all sizes):
The row counts reset above the hem fold.
Row 1 (rs, includes buttonhole): kfb, k2, k2tog, yo2, ssk, k10 (11, 12, 12, 13, 14, 15, 16), m1r, k2, m1l, k109 (118, 126, 137, 145, 154, 162, 173), m1r, k2, m1l, k17 (18, 19, 19, 20, 21, 22, 23).

Row 2 (ws, includes buttonhole): p to 7 st from end, ptbl, p1, ptbl, p3, pfb.

Row 3: kfb, k19 (20, 21, 21, 22, 23, 24, 25), m1r, k2, m1l, k111 (120, 129, 138, 146, 155, 164, 173), m1r, k2, m1l, k18 (19, 20, 20, 21, 22, 23, 24). Total stitches: 158 (169, 179, 190, 200, 211, 221, 232)

Row 4: p to last st, pfb.

Place side seam markers:
Row 5: kfb, k45 (48, 50, 53, 55, 58, 61, 63), pm, k74 (79, 84, 90, 95, 100, 105, 111), pm, k to end.

Row 6: p to last stitch, pfb.

Row 7 (includes buttonhole): kfb, k2, k2tog, yo2, ssk, k to end.

Row 8 (includes buttonhole): p to 7 st from end, ptbl, p1, ptbl, p3, pfb.

Bust Shaping:
Cup Size A:
Row 9 (rs): kfb, k to end.
Row 10 (ws): p to 1 st from end, pfb.

Cup Sizes B (C, D, E, F):
Work Side Bust Darts

Right Dart:
Row 9: kfb, k to 1 stitch before side seam marker. Wrap and turn.

Purl 15 (17, 20, 23, 25) stitches. Wrap and turn.

Work to 3 (2, 2, 1, 1) stitches before previously wrapped stitch, wrap and turn.

Repeat this row 3 (7, 9, 13, 17) times, ending with a ws row. Turn work. Knit across wrapped stitches, picking up wraps and knitting them together with the wrapped stitch, to side seam marker, sm, knit across back to left side seam marker.

Left Dart:
Slip marker, knit 16 (18, 21, 24, 26) stitches, wrap and turn.

Purl 15 (17, 20, 23, 25) stitches, wrap and turn.

Work to 3 (2, 2, 1, 1) stitches before previously wrapped stitch, wrap and turn.

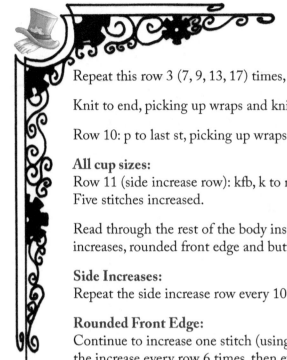

Repeat this row 3 (7, 9, 13, 17) times, ending with a ws row.

Knit to end, picking up wraps and knitting them together with the wrapped stitch.

Row 10: p to last st, picking up wraps and purling them together with the wrapped stitch, pfb.

All cup sizes:
Row 11 (side increase row): kfb, k to marker, m1r, sm, m1l, work to marker, m1r, sm, m1l, knit to end. Five stitches increased.

Read through the rest of the body instructions. You will be working all three techniques (side increases, rounded front edge and buttonholes) at the same time while you continue the body.

Side Increases:
Repeat the side increase row every 10 (10, 10, 10, 10, 6, 6, 6) rows 2 (2, 2, 2, 2, 5, 5, 5) times.

Rounded Front Edge:
Continue to increase one stitch (using kfb or pfb) at the right front edge. Starting on Row 12, work the increase every row 6 times, then every other row 9 times. Work even (no increases) for 4 rows. Work decrease at right edge (k2tog or p2tog) every other row 9 times, then every row 17 times. You will be working these increases and decreases while working all other body instructions, until the total body length is 10 inches. Once you split the body into fronts and back, the increases/decreases for the rounded front edge will all be worked on the right front.

Buttonholes:
Work buttonhole row (See Special Techniques) every 6 rows 10 times (this begins after the first two buttonholes are completed). You will be adding buttonholes on the correct rows while working all other body instructions. Buttonhole rows: 1, 7, 13, 19, 25, 31, 37, 43, 49, 55, 61, 67.

While working the preceding three instructions, continue to work body in stockinette as established until piece measures 5½ inches from the bottom of

the folded hem. At this point you will split the body into fronts and back, continuing to work the rounded front edge and the buttonholes in addition to the fronts and back instructions.

Total stitches (after side increases and completing the increases for the right front edge): 194 (205, 215, 226, 236, 256, 266, 277)

Right Front:
Total right front stitches: 69 (72, 74, 77, 79, 84, 88, 90)
You should have two increases left to perform for the rounded front edge.

NOTE: If your row gauge is off, your stitch count may differ due to the rounded edge shaping. Use the side seam marker to determine the front edge stitches.

Knit to marker, remove marker and turn work.
ws: BO 5 sts, work to end.
rs: knit across.
ws: BO 3 sts, work to end.
rs: knit to 3 stitches before end, k2tog, k1.

Repeat decrease every right side row 3 (3, 3, 4, 5, 6, 7, 8) more times. Total stitches: 61 (64, 66, 68, 69, 74, 76, 77)

Work until piece measures 10 inches, ending with a ws row. You should have just finished the rounded front edge shaping.

BO 8 (8, 9, 9, 9, 9, 9, 9) stitches at right front edge, k to end.
Purl 1 row.
BO 2 (3, 4, 4, 4, 5, 6, 5) stitches at right front edge every right side row 3 times.
Purl 1 row.
Bind off.

Back:
Total back stitches: 80 (85, 90, 96, 101, 109, 114, 120)
Separate the back from the left front stitches and work the following instructions on the back stitches.
BO 5 sts at beginning of the next two rows.
BO 3 sts at beginning of the next two rows.
K1, ssk, k to 3 sts before end, k2tog, k1.

Repeat decrease every right side row 3 (3, 3, 4, 5, 6, 7, 8) more times. Total stitches: 56 (61, 66, 70, 73, 79, 82, 86)
Work until piece measures 11 inches.
Bind off.

Left Front:
Total stitches left front: 43 (46, 49, 51, 54, 60, 62, 65)
Remove marker, BO 5 sts, work to end.
Purl 1 row.
BO 3 sts, work to end.

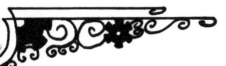

Purl 1 row.
K1, ssk, k to end.

Repeat decrease every right side row 3 (3, 3, 4, 5, 6, 7, 8) more times. Total stitches: 31 (34, 37, 38, 40, 45, 46, 48)

Work until piece measures 10 inches, ending with rs row.

ws: BO 8 (8, 9, 9, 9, 9, 9) stitches at left front edge, p to end.
Knit 1 row.
BO 2 (3, 4, 4, 4, 5, 6, 5) stitches at left front edge every wrong side row 3 times.
Knit 1 row.
Bind off.

Sleeves:
Cast on 33 (33, 35, 35, 37, 37, 39, 41) stitches provisionally (any method).

Place marker and join to work in the round. Be careful not to twist.

Knit 2 rows stockinette

Begin Chain Pattern (see Special Techniques):
K14 (14, 15, 15, 16, 16, 17, 18), pm, chain pattern (over 5 sts), pm, k14 (14, 15, 15, 16, 16, 17, 18).
Continue working the chain pattern between the markers, working stockinette otherwise for 6 (6, 6, 4, 4, 4, 4, 4) rows.

Start increases:
Increase row: kfb, k to marker, sm, work chain pattern, sm, k to last 2 sts, kfb, k1.

Continue to work in pattern as established, and repeat increase row every 7 (7, 7, 5, 5, 5, 5, 5) rows 8 (9, 9, 11, 11, 11, 11, 11) more times.
Total stitches: 51 (53, 55, 59, 61, 61, 63, 65)
Total length: 9"

Elbow:
Repeat increase row every other row 4 (4, 5, 5, 5, 6, 6, 6) times. Total stitches: 59 (61, 65, 69, 71, 73, 75, 77)

Work Bicep Section:
Increase row: kfb twice, k to 2 sts before marker, k2tog, sm, work chain pattern, sm, ssk, k to last 3 sts, kfb twice, k1.

Repeat the increase row 1 (1, 1, 2, 2, 2, 3, 3) more times, for a total of 2 (2, 2, 3, 3, 3, 4, 4) increase rows. Total stitches: 63 (65, 69, 75, 77, 79, 83, 85)

Balanced chain pattern: kfb, k to 2 sts before marker, k2tog, sm, work chain pattern, sm, ssk, k to last 2 sts, kfb, k1.

Work until sleeve measures 16½" at beginning of round (underarm), ending with a ws row. The chain stitch portion of the sleeve will be 1½ to 2 inches shorter due to the fabric bias.

Begin Puff Shoulder:
Increase row: kfb, *k1, m1r,* rep between * to 2 sts before marker, k2tog, sm, work chain, sm, ssk, *k1, m1r,* rep between * to last 2 sts, kfb, k1. Total stitches: 113 (117, 126, 138, 142, 146, 155, 157)

Begin to work flat, continuing chain pattern and working the other stitches in stockinette.

Begin Armhole Shaping:
BO 5 sts at beginning of next two rows.
BO 3 sts at beginning of next two rows.
Total stitches: 97 (101, 110, 122, 126, 130, 139, 141)

RS decrease row:
K to 2 sts before marker, k2tog, sm, work chain pattern, sm, ssk, k to end.

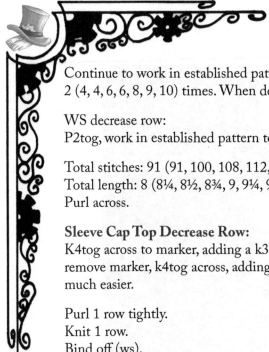

Continue to work in established pattern, and repeat decrease row every 20 (12, 13, 9, 10, 8, 7, 6) rows 2 (4, 4, 6, 6, 8, 9, 10) times. When decrease row falls on a purl row, perform the following:

WS decrease row:
P2tog, work in established pattern to last 2 stitches, p2tog.

Total stitches: 91 (91, 100, 108, 112, 112, 119, 119)
Total length: 8 (8¼, 8½, 8¾, 9, 9¼, 9½, 9½)"
Purl across.

Sleeve Cap Top Decrease Row:
K4tog across to marker, adding a k3tog or k5tog if needed, remove marker, k5tog (chain stitches), remove marker, k4tog across, adding a k3tog or k5tog if needed. A crochet hook will make this row much easier.

Purl 1 row tightly.
Knit 1 row.
Bind off (ws).

Sleeve Ruffle:
Unravel provisional cast on and pick up stitches.

Working in the round, kfb around.
Work stockinette for 2" (16 rows).
Bind off.

Body Ruffle:
Sew shoulders together with back.

The ruffle is added to the right front and entire neck. With rs facing, pick up stitches starting at right side seam - directly below the center of the right armhole. Pick up stitches evenly along bottom (one row above hem fold), along rounded front edge, around right neck, across back, across left neck, ending at left neck opening edge.

ws: pfb across.
Knit stockinette for 2" (16 rows).
Bind off pwise (ws).

FINISHING:
Attach sleeves to body, centering the sleeve cap top on the shoulder seam. The puff sleeve requires you to pleat the sleeve fabric as you attach it to the armhole.

Sew buttons onto the left front to line up with right front buttonholes.

Attach neck ribbon as follows: sew top edge of ribbon to inside of ruffle, approximately 1½" below the BO edge. Sew bottom edge of ribbon approx 1" below the BO edge of the body, creating tension in the ribbon. This should help the collar ruffle stand up straight and create a nicely finished inside collar.

The Parquet Underbust Corset

By: Sarra Loew

DESCRIPTION:
Underbust corset, knit bottom up with a vertical chevron stitch pattern. Pick up stitches along edges and knit eyelet section for lacing.

FINISHED DIMENSIONS:
Width: 22½ (25, 27½, 30, 32½, 35, 37½, 40, 42½)"
Length: 8 (8, 8, 9, 9, 9, 10, 10, 10)"

Note: Length will shrink 1-3 inches due to negative ease. Should fit from natural waist to underbust.

TO FIT BODY MEASUREMENTS:
Underbust: 27-28 (29-30, 31-33, 34-35, 36-38, 39-40, 41-43, 44-46, 46-48)"

EASE:
4-5 inches negative ease

A Lady is always at the height of fashion... but she is certainly going to get there on her own terms! This elegant chevron motif provides gentle shaping, so you can achieve the desired silhouette in comfort and style. Form and function fit together beautifully as you glide across the ballroom floor, the picture of effortless grace.

YARN AND YARDAGE:
Serenity Silk III by Zen Yarn Garden,
http://zenyarngarden.co
75% merino, 15% cashmere, 10% silk; 450yds (412m) per 115g fingering weight
Color: Velvet, 1 (1, 1, 1, 2, 2, 2, 2, 3) skeins

GAUGE:
Knitted and blocked gauge:
In stockinette: 30 sts x 42 rows = 4"/10cm
In pattern: 36 sts x 42 rows = 4"/10cm

NEEDLES AND NOTIONS:
24-42" (depending on size knit) size 3 US/3.25mm circular needle
3-6 yds ½" ribbon for lacing
6 yds ¾" ribbon for boning casement
80-180" ½" plastic boning, depending on size made

Pattern

Body:
Cast on 191 (212, 233, 254, 275, 296, 317, 338, 359) stitches.
ws: purl across.

Begin working pattern:
rs: k1, *kfb, k8, sl2tog kwise, k1, p2sso, k7, kfb, k1,* repeat between * 9 (10, 11, 12, 13, 14, 15, 16, 17) times, k1.

ws: purl across.

Repeat these last two rows until piece measures 8 (8, 8, 9, 9, 9, 10, 10, 10) inches, measured along the kfb column, not from the points.

NOTE: If you are adjusting the height, remember that the height will shrink 1-3 inches when worn depending on how much negative ease you used.

I-Cord Top Edging:
Using cable cast on, CO 3 stitches.
K2, k2tog, slip those 3 stitches back to left needle. Repeat until all stitches are bound off.

Linen Stitch Lacing Edging:
With rs facing, pick up 63
(63, 63, 71, 71, 71, 79, 79, 79)
stitches along right side edge
starting at bottom edge.
Purl 1 row.

Row 1: k1, *sl1wyif, k1*.
Row 2: k1, p1, *sl1wyib, p1,*
k1.
Row 3: k2 (2, 2, 0, 0, 0, 3, 3, 3),
k3, yo, k2tog,, k1.
Row 4: purl.

Repeat Rows 1 and 2 once
more.

Bind off tightly with yarn held
doubled.

Pick up the same number of
stitches on the left side edge,
starting at the bottom edge
Knit 1 row.

Row 1: k1, p1, *sl1wyib, p1,*
k1.
Row 2: k1, *sl1wyif, k1*.
Row 3: p2 (2, 2, 0, 0, 0, 3, 3, 3),
p3, yo, p2tog, p1.
Row 4: knit.

Repeat Rows 1 and 2 once
more.

Bind off tightly with yarn held
doubled.

FINISHING:
Cut boning into 8 (8, 8, 9, 9, 9, 10, 10, 10) inch pieces. Cut boning casement ribbon into 11 (11,
11,12, 12, 12, 13, 13, 13) inch pieces. Sew boning casement ribbon into corset back along the
decrease line, from the tip of the point all the way to the top. Insert boning into ribbon casement and
sew closed.

Lace the lacing ribbons through the eyelets in the lacing pattern you prefer.

The Gossip Stole

By: Amanda Williams

DESCRIPTION:
This lace scarf knit from lace weight yarn makes an excellent veil for your top hat or could be a stole if made in a fingering yarn instead. The pattern uses both a knit-on edging and an edging that is created as you knit the body.

FINISHED DIMENSIONS:
16½" x 66"

YARN AND YARDAGE:
Zephyr Lace by The Painted Tiger, http://ThePaintedTiger.com 50% silk, 50% merino; 1200yds (1100m) per 115g; lace weight Color: Abyss, 1 skein

Who was that lovely, mysterious woman? As an airy, delicate veil lightly cascading from your hat or draped becomingly around bare shoulders as a stole, you'll be an ethereal beauty, leaving behind a buzz of excited whispers. This eye-catching lace, and the lady wearing it, are sure to be the talk of the party!

GAUGE:
Ball band gauge of chosen yarn: 33-40 sts = 4"
Knitted and unblocked gauge:
In stockinette: 34 sts x 44 rows = 4 in/10cm
Knitted and blocked gauge:
In stockinette: 24 sts x 38 rows = 4 in/10cm

NEEDLES AND NOTIONS:
Size 3 US/3.25mm needles (long enough to accommodate all stitches)

PATTERN NOTES:
If you prefer a larger or smaller size you may choose any weight and gauge you like and adjust the number of chart repeats as you see fit.

This is a challenging lace pattern. Stitch markers are indispensable. You should place a stitch marker between each lace section, including each repeat and edgings.

Each border chart repeat corresponds to one body chart repeat. You can make the scarf as large or small as you like by adjusting the number of chart repetitions.

View the schematic for a picture of where the charts are placed and the direction of knitting for each.

You will begin by knitting the first half of a mitered corner top down. You will then hold those stitches while you pick up

and knit the stitches along the mitered edge. Next, you knit the second half of the mitered corner, followed by the edging for the bottom edge. At the end of the bottom edging, you will knit both halves of the next mitered corner. Then you pick up stitches along the bottom edging and work across the held stitches from the beginning of the work.

You will start the body of the piece next. You will work the body of the piece, including the edging, until it reaches your desired length.

The third mitered corner is only worked on the 10 rightmost stitches of the piece, with the second half of that corner worked as for the second corner. The top edging is worked as knitted-on edging, and finally, the first half of the fourth mitered corner is worked. The stitches along the slanted edge are picked up and the last mitered corner is completed.

Pattern

Cast on 2 stitches.

Work Chart A once. This is the first half of the first corner.

Put stitches on holder.

With rs facing, rotate clockwise 90 degrees, then pick up and knit 10 stitches evenly along full length of the slanted edge. This turns the work and begins the bottom border.

Beginning with a ws row for Row 1, **work Chart B.** This is the second half of first corner. NOTE: You will begin by working only the first stitch on your needle. As you work, you will work more and more of the stitches on your right needle.

Work Chart C 6 times. This is the bottom edging.

Work Chart D once. This is the first half of second corner. NOTE: As you work the chart, you will work fewer and fewer of the stitches on your needle. This creates the miter shaping when you work the next chart.

Work Chart B once. This is the second half of second corner. NOTE: You will begin by

working only the first stitch on your needle. As you work you will work more and more of the stitches on your right needle.

Pick up and purl 72 stitches (12 for each repeat of Chart C) across. You may wish to place stitch markers every 12 stitches to mark your chart repeats. Purl across the 10 held stitches from the end of Chart A

You now have 92 stitches on your needles.

Work Chart E 27 times or until piece is the desired length.
Right side is facing.

Work Chart F on the first 10 stitches of the row. This is the first half of the 3rd corner. NOTE: As you work the chart, you will work fewer and fewer of the stitches on your needle. This creates the miter shaping when you work the next chart.

Work Chart G once. This is the second half of the 3rd corner.
NOTE: You will begin by working only the first stitch on your needle. As you work you will work more and more of the stitches on your right needle.

Work Chart H 6 times across the top of the piece. NOTE: As you work, you will be knitting together with held stitches from Chart E to create a knitted on edging. Pay close attention as there are both p2tog and p3tog stitches used for this.

Work Chart F once. This is the first half of 4th corner.
NOTE: As you work the chart, you will work fewer and fewer of the stitches on your needle. This

creates the miter shaping when you work the next chart.
Sl1, k8.

Work Chart I once. This is the last half of the 4th corner.
NOTE: As you work you will be knitting together with held stitches from the previous Chart F.

Break yarn and pull tail through last remaining stitch.

CHART NOTES:
Pay close attention to the increases that happen on ws rows 4, 8, 12, and 18 of Chart E.

FINISHING:
Weave in ends, block agressively and wear.

Charts

Chart A

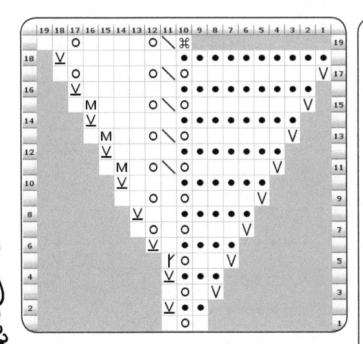

Legend:

No Stitch
RS: Placeholder - No stitch made.
WS: none defined

knit
RS: knit stitch
WS: purl stitch

yo
RS: Yarn Over
WS: Yarn Over

purl
RS: purl stitch
WS: knit stitch

slip wyif
RS: Slip stitch as if to purl, with yarn in front
WS: Slip stitch as if to purl, with yarn in back

slip
RS: Slip stitch as if to purl, holding yarn in back
WS: Slip stitch as if to purl, holding yarn in front

kfb
RS: Knit into the front and back of the stitch
WS: Purl into the front and the back of the stitch

ssk
RS: Slip one stitch as if to knit, Slip another stitch as if to knit, Insert left-hand needle into front of these 2 stitches and knit them together
WS: Purl two stitches together in back loops, inserting needle from the left, behind and into the backs of the 2nd & 1st stitches in that order

make one
RS: Make one by lifting strand in between stitch just worked and the next stitch, knit into back of this thread.
WS: Make one by lifting strand in between stitch just worked and the next stitch, purl into back of this thread.

Knit 1 Pass 9 Over
RS: Knit 1, Pass 9 sts on left needle over the just completed knit stitch.
WS:

Chart B

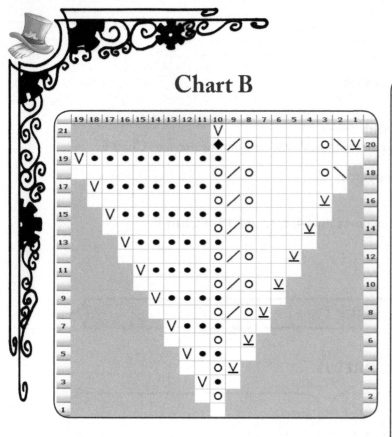

Chart C

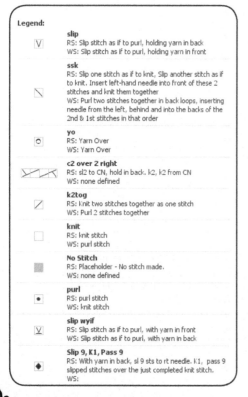

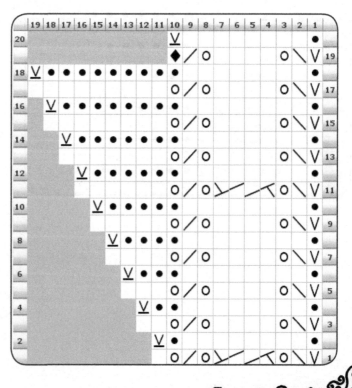

Chart D

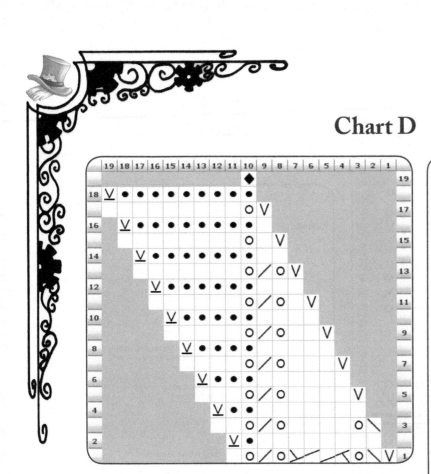

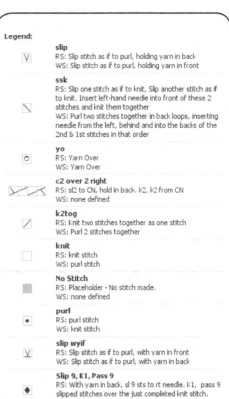

Legend:

$\underline{V}$	**slip**	RS: Slip stitch as if to purl, holding yarn in back WS: Slip stitch as if to purl, holding yarn in front
$\diagdown$	**ssk**	RS: Slip one stitch as if to knit, Slip another stitch as if to knit. Insert left-hand needle into front of these 2 stitches and knit them together WS: Purl two stitches together in back loops, inserting needle from the left, behind and into the backs of the 2nd & 1st stitches in that order
O	**yo**	RS: Yarn Over WS: Yarn Over
	c2 over 2 right	RS: sl2 to CN, hold in back. k2, k2 from CN WS: none defined
$\diagup$	**k2tog**	RS: Knit two stitches together as one stitch WS: Purl 2 stitches together
	knit	RS: knit stitch WS: purl stitch
	No Stitch	RS: Placeholder - No stitch made. WS: none defined
•	**purl**	RS: purl stitch WS: knit stitch
$\underline{V}$	**slip wyif**	RS: Slip stitch as if to purl, with yarn in front WS: Slip stitch as if to purl, with yarn in back
♦	**Slip 9, K1, Pass 9**	RS: With yarn in back, sl 9 sts to rt needle. K1, pass 9 slipped stitches over the just completed knit stitch. WS:

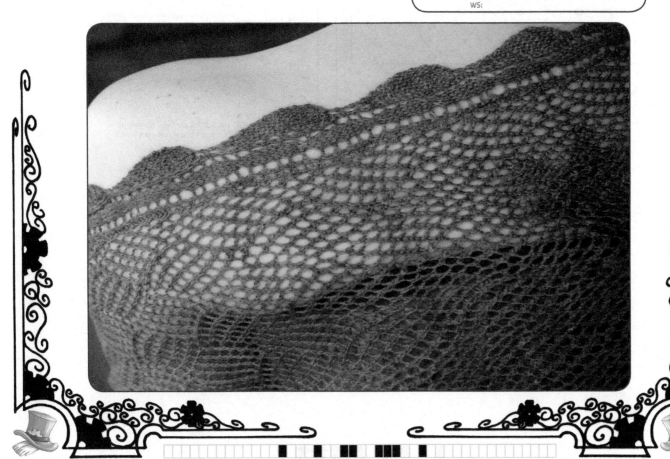

Chart E

Chart rotated clockwise

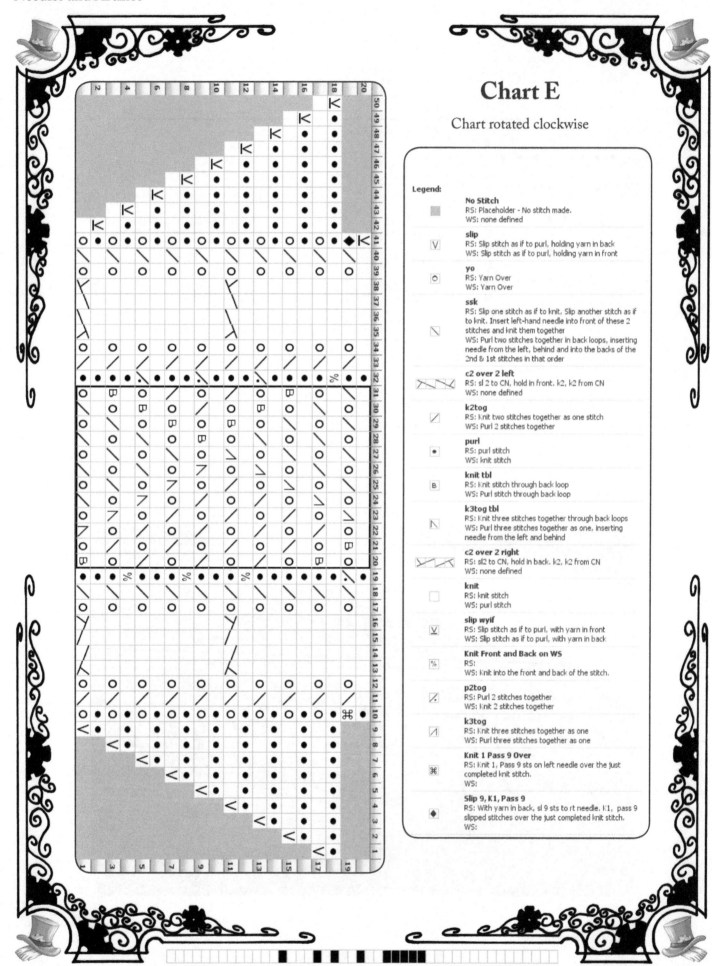

Legend:

	No Stitch	RS: Placeholder - No stitch made. WS: none defined
V	**slip**	RS: Slip stitch as if to purl, holding yarn in back WS: Slip stitch as if to purl, holding yarn in front
O	**yo**	RS: Yarn Over WS: Yarn Over
⟍	**ssk**	RS: Slip one stitch as if to knit, Slip another stitch as if to knit. Insert left-hand needle into front of these 2 stitches and knit them together WS: Purl two stitches together in back loops, inserting needle from the left, behind and into the backs of the 2nd & 1st stitches in that order
⤬	**c2 over 2 left**	RS: sl 2 to CN, hold in front. k2, k2 from CN WS: none defined
⟋	**k2tog**	RS: Knit two stitches together as one stitch WS: Purl 2 stitches together
•	**purl**	RS: purl stitch WS: knit stitch
B	**knit tbl**	RS: Knit stitch through back loop WS: Purl stitch through back loop
⟍	**k3tog tbl**	RS: Knit three stitches together through back loops WS: Purl three stitches together as one, inserting needle from the left and behind
⤬	**c2 over 2 right**	RS: sl2 to CN, hold in back. k2, k2 from CN WS: none defined
	knit	RS: knit stitch WS: purl stitch
V	**slip wyif**	RS: Slip stitch as if to purl, with yarn in front WS: Slip stitch as if to purl, with yarn in back
%	**Knit Front and Back on WS**	RS: WS: Knit into the front and back of the stitch.
⟋•	**p2tog**	RS: Purl 2 stitches together WS: Knit 2 stitches together
⟋	**k3tog**	RS: Knit three stitches together as one WS: Purl three stitches together as one
⌘	**Knit 1 Pass 9 Over**	RS: Knit 1, Pass 9 sts on left needle over the just completed knit stitch. WS:
◆	**Slip 9, K1, Pass 9**	RS: With yarn in back, sl 9 sts to rt needle. K1, pass 9 slipped stitches over the just completed knit stitch. WS:

Chart F

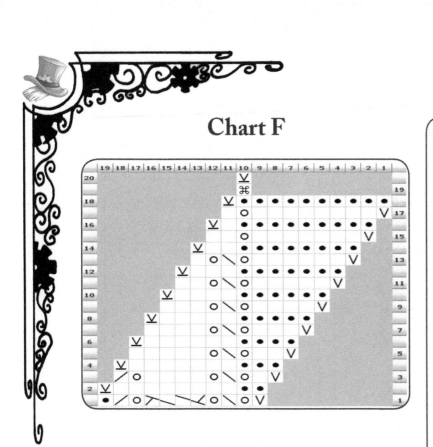

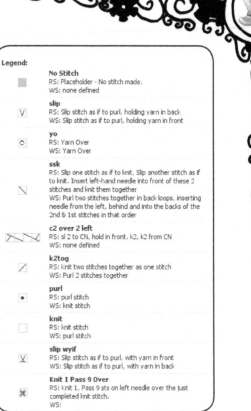

Legend:

No Stitch
RS: Placeholder - No stitch made.
WS: none defined

slip
RS: Slip stitch as if to purl, holding yarn in back
WS: Slip stitch as if to purl, holding yarn in front

yo
RS: Yarn Over
WS: Yarn Over

ssk
RS: Slip one stitch as if to knit, Slip another stitch as if to knit. Insert left-hand needle into front of these 2 stitches and knit them together
WS: Purl two stitches together in back loops, inserting needle from the left, behind and into the backs of the 2nd & 1st stitches in that order

c2 over 2 left
RS: sl 2 to CN, hold in front, k2, k2 from CN
WS: none defined

k2tog
RS: knit two stitches together as one stitch
WS: Purl 2 stitches together

purl
RS: purl stitch
WS: knit stitch

knit
RS: knit stitch
WS: purl stitch

slip wyif
RS: Slip stitch as if to purl, with yarn in front
WS: Slip stitch as if to purl, with yarn in back

Knit 1 Pass 9 Over
RS: Knit 1, Pass 9 sts on left needle over the just completed knit stitch.
WS:

Chart G

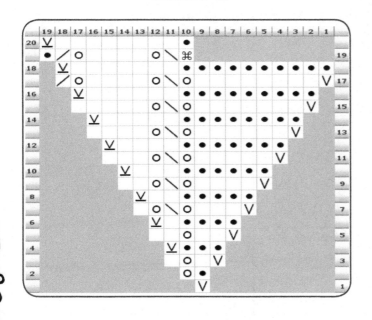

Legend:

No Stitch
RS: Placeholder - No stitch made.
WS: none defined

slip
RS: Slip stitch as if to purl, holding yarn in back
WS: Slip stitch as if to purl, holding yarn in front

purl
RS: purl stitch
WS: knit stitch

yo
RS: Yarn Over
WS: Yarn Over

knit
RS: knit stitch
WS: purl stitch

slip wyif
RS: Slip stitch as if to purl, with yarn in front
WS: Slip stitch as if to purl, with yarn in back

ssk
RS: Slip one stitch as if to knit, Slip another stitch as if to knit. Insert left-hand needle into front of these 2 stitches and knit them together
WS: Purl two stitches together in back loops, inserting needle from the left, behind and into the backs of the 2nd & 1st stitches in that order

k2tog
RS: knit two stitches together as one stitch
WS: Purl 2 stitches together

Knit 1 Pass 9 Over
RS: Knit 1, Pass 9 sts on left needle over the just completed knit stitch.
WS:

Chart H

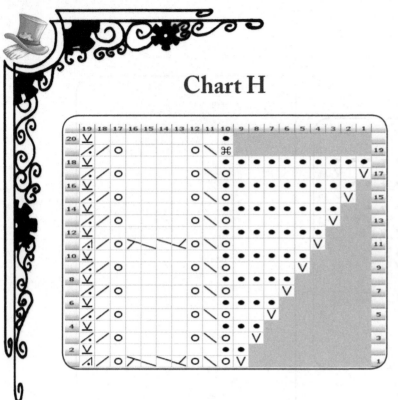

Legend:

	No Stitch	RS: Placeholder - No stitch made. WS: none defined
V	**slip**	RS: Slip stitch as if to purl, holding yarn in back WS: Slip stitch as if to purl, holding yarn in front
O	**yo**	RS: Yarn Over WS: Yarn Over
⟍	**ssk**	RS: Slip one stitch as if to knit, Slip another stitch as if to knit. Insert left-hand needle into front of these 2 stitches and knit them together WS: Purl two stitches together in back loops, inserting needle from the left, behind and into the backs of the 2nd & 1st stitches in that order
⟋⟍	**c2 over 2 left**	RS: sl 2 to CN, hold in front. k2, k2 from CN WS: none defined
⟋	**k2tog**	RS: knit two stitches together as one stitch WS: Purl 2 stitches together
⟋	**p3tog**	RS: Purl three stitches together as one WS: Knit three stitches together as one
•	**purl**	RS: purl stitch WS: knit stitch
	knit	RS: knit stitch WS: purl stitch
V	**slip wyif**	RS: Slip stitch as if to purl, with yarn in front WS: Slip stitch as if to purl, with yarn in back
⟋	**p2tog**	RS: Purl 2 stitches together WS: Knit 2 stitches together
⌘	**Knit 1 Pass 9 Over**	RS: knit 1, Pass 9 sts on left needle over the just completed knit stitch. WS:

Chart I

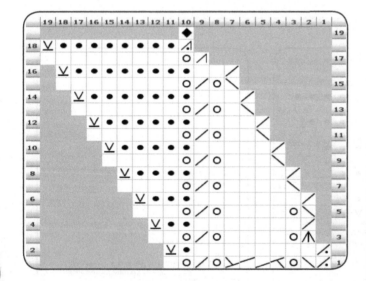

Legend:

⟋	**p2tog**	RS: Purl 2 stitches together WS: Knit 2 stitches together
⟍	**ssk**	RS: Slip one stitch as if to knit, Slip another stitch as if to knit. Insert left-hand needle into front of these 2 stitches and knit them together WS: Purl two stitches together in back loops, inserting needle from the left, behind and into the backs of the 2nd & 1st stitches in that order
O	**yo**	RS: Yarn Over WS: Yarn Over
⟋⟍	**c2 over 2 right**	RS: sl2 to CN, hold in back. k2, k2 from CN WS: none defined
⟋	**k2tog**	RS: knit two stitches together as one stitch WS: Purl 2 stitches together
	knit	RS: knit stitch WS: purl stitch
	No Stitch	RS: Placeholder - No stitch made. WS: none defined
•	**purl**	RS: purl stitch WS: knit stitch
V	**slip wyif**	RS: Slip stitch as if to purl, with yarn in front WS: Slip stitch as if to purl, with yarn in back
⋀	**Central Double Dec**	RS: Slip first and second stitches together as if to knit. Knit 1 stitch. Pass two slipped stitches over the knit stitch. WS: Slip first and second stitches together as it to purl through the back loop. Purl 1 stitch. Pass two slipped stitches over the purl stitch.
⟋	**k3tog**	RS: knit three stitches together as one WS: Purl three stitches together as one
⟋	**p3tog**	RS: Purl three stitches together as one WS: Knit three stitches together as one
◆	**Slip 9, K1, Pass 9**	RS: With yarn in back, sl 9 sts to rt needle. k1, pass 9 slipped stitches over the just completed knit stitch. WS:

Chapter Five - High Society

Schematic

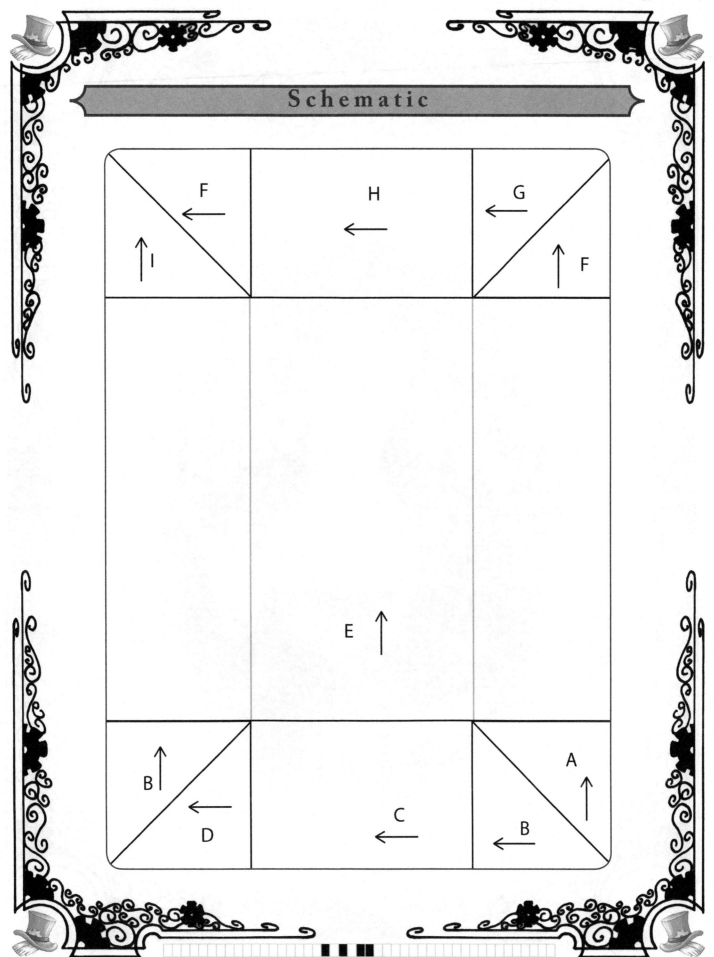

Chapter Six

In which arses are kicked

In the twilight, the narrow and near-silent airship was almost impossible to see. Somehow the eye shifted away from it. If Kristoff concentrated, it would suddenly pop into perfect view, but once he turned his eyes away, it faded into the background once again. He shook his head and turned to Coraline. "Your Mr. Tingley is an amazing inventor. I've never seen anything like it. How does it work?"

Coraline laughed. "You won't ever see anything like it, and you won't get the secret out of me!" Her merry smile faded away as she looked over the rest of the Ladies, decked out for espionage and carrying a variety of weapons from the ship's armory. Anna had refused the new wardrobe, as she thought that changing clothes more than once a day was utterly stupid and had said so quite loudly. Miriam had the small flock of jungle sheep on halters, and was wearing a determined expression.

Coraline cleared her throat. "All right everyone, time to go! Kristoff, the Ladies will help you and Anna to your destination. Peter will stay with Lilith Ascending in case a quick escape is required." Peter nodded politely to the assembled adventurers, and the other Ladies stepped a short distance away to allow Coraline a touch of privacy as she wished him farewell. Alyssa smiled knowingly as Coraline rejoined the group, a hint of a blush on her cheeks, and a large bag in her hands.

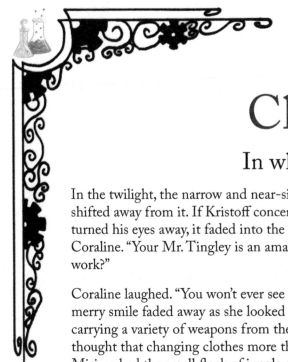

Dr. Erma Melanogaster's devotion to Science was unparalleled among the Ladies. She was so engrossed in her work that the Ladies took turns making sure she remembered to eat, and often had to physically remove her from her lab to make her attend their social events. With just a small amount of grumbling, Dr. Erma enjoyed the enforced company, especially when she was able to discuss her latest theories. Her Universal Theory of Color Coordinating Knitwear Accessories made headlines in both scientific and fashion newspapers. While her keen intellect could unravel the most tangled mysteries, she occasionally forgot to take care of simple matters such as making sure her jumper was on right-side out.

"Right, then!" Anna said cheerfully. "Let's go storm the castle!"

****

"A hedge wall? He grew a hedge wall? What the devil is this, some kind of fairy tale?" Kristoff glared at the impenetrable foliage in front of him. "Who plants a hedge as a defense mechanism, anyway? It seems terribly inefficient. I can just climb over."

"You could if that hedge wasn't Aquifolium Belladonna," Caldonia's voice took on a lecturing quality. "It's incredibly poisonous to humans. If you don't handle it with waxed leather gear, you will quickly absorb the toxins and there's no cure for that. I have a pair of waxed leather gloves, but they wouldn't provide the level of protection required. You'd need a full suit."

There was a pause as everyone took a step back from the hedge.

"Does anyone, by chance, have a waxed leather suit with them?" Anna asked hopefully. Everyone glared at her, and she shrugged. "I can hope, can't I?"

Kristoff sighed. "I suppose we'll just have to walk around to the front gate, then. That seems anti-climactic somehow."

"You could do that if you want. However, I believe our hooved companions can assist!" Theodosia smiled proudly. "In my studies I discovered that they are naturally immune to every plant poison I could find. And there are rather a lot of poisonous plants in the Amazon! Including one that bears a close resemblance to this hedge! Miriam, release the sheep!"

Miriam met Kristoff's eyes, smiled brightly, and dropped the halter leads on the small flock of jungle sheep she had insisted on bringing. The little herbivores sprang into action, heading straight for the hedge and devouring it with determination and speed. Miriam clapped her hands together in glee. "Look at them go! They just love grazing on trees and bushes. I told you we needed to bring the sheep!"

Kristoff shook his head as he watched the wee little sheep grazing a hole deep into the hedge. "I capitulate. We did need the sheep. We shall bring them everywhere we go from now on. We may even find something for them to defecate on." He paused. "They're quite efficient eaters, aren't they?" The hole was nearly through to the other side now.

Anna rolled her eyes. "They've been on an airship eating hay for the last two days. Peter just put in the grain trough yesterday. I'm sure they were dreaming of fresh greens! Good job, Arcadibaa!" The little sheep she'd claimed as her own burst through to the other side of the hedge and ate a doorway into it. Theodosia and Miriam shared a glance and nodded in satisfaction.

"Now, you can go through, but do be careful not to touch the sides or the top. Your shoes will be enough to protect you from any poison on the ground."

Jungle Sheep   (male : juvenile)

Caldonia reached into her satchel and pulled out a pair of waxed leather gloves. "I will stay behind. The sheep must be decontaminated before they're allowed back onto the airship, and I don't think they nor I will do well in any sort of combat." Anna darted in and gave Caldonia a quick hug before crouching down to sneak through the hedge with the rest of the group.

Once inside, Erma held up her hand and they all paused. She scanned the manicured grounds methodically, then turned to the others. "Klaus has defenses set up. There are devices that scan the

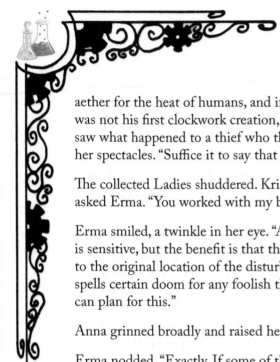

aether for the heat of humans, and if we're picked up an alarm will sound. The simulacrum of Anna was not his first clockwork creation, either! The early prototypes have all been turned into guards. I saw what happened to a thief who thought to rob the place." She paused, her face paling a bit behind her spectacles. "Suffice it to say that I was unable to eat for several days."

The collected Ladies shuddered. Kristoff bit his lip. "How do you suggest we infiltrate, then?" he asked Erma. "You worked with my brother. What are the weaknesses in the system?"

Erma smiled, a twinkle in her eye. "Ah, you're clever. You ask the correct questions! The alarm system is sensitive, but the benefit is that the clockwork guards are not intelligent. They all deploy at once, to the original location of the disturbance. This means they can be drawn out into one place, which spells certain doom for any foolish thieves, but we are not foolish thieves. We are forewarned, and we can plan for this."

Anna grinned broadly and raised her rifle. "We need a diversion!"

Erma nodded. "Exactly. If some of the party engage the automata on this side of the building, others of us can sneak in around the other side. With luck, we can reach Klaus and his clockwork doll before he even realizes there are two teams."

Anna frowned. Alyssa patted her on the arm. "I know it's difficult for you, deciding whether to shoot clockwork guards or go punch Klaus in the face. You really should go help your fiancé, though. There will probably be something to shoot inside." Anna brightened up considerably.

Kristoff nodded. "All right. Anna and I will head around to the other side of the mansion. Give us five minutes, Ladies, and then breach the security. Once we hear the alarms, we'll make for the building and find our way to Klaus."

"Wait!" Coraline interrupted. "Erma mentioned something about clockworks, so I brought a new toy Peter and Mr. Tingley have been working together on." Coraline seemed quite excited about the weapon's prospects. "It's a grenade that contains a large amount of energy."

Erma leaned closer. "What is the storage mechanism? And what have you constructed the shell out of? And how did you gather the energy?" She took a breath and was about to continue with her questions.

Anna slapped a hand over Erma's mouth. "Later, Erma. Coraline, how do they work?"

Coraline nodded. "When there is a group of clockworks assembled, throw this at the ground near their feet to break it. The released energy should heat up and break their control functions, which should cause them to stop running. They might explode - we haven't been able to do much testing. Oh, and you should probably be far away when they break- they are most likely quite dangerous to people as well."

The Ladies nodded solemnly while Coraline handed the spheres out. When everyone had one tucked away, Coraline nodded and dropped the empty bag.

"I'll be joining Kristoff and Anna," Erma said calmly. "I know the inside layout and the location of the labs." She turned to Theodosia, Miriam, Alyssa and Coraline. "All you need to do to trigger the alarm is to walk toward the building. Once you are within range, you will be detected. The guards are powerful but they cannot strategize. Work together, attack the joints, and you should be able to overcome them. Good luck!" There was a moment of hugging and whispered wishes of goodwill, then the two parties split and the sneak attack team headed off into the night, keeping to the shadows of the hedge.

Erma broke the silence after a few moments. "There is something you should know." She paused, considering her words carefully. "I imagine you know that your brother keeps his clockwork woman as a slave. You probably consider this a great injustice and wish to see her freed. However, I also know that she is required to be loyal to Klaus, and is theoretically a great danger to us. We may wish to find and subdue her first." Erma held up her hand to forestall Anna's immediate dissent. "I say this rationally, as a scientist. She is an exceedingly powerful variable, and we stand a much better chance of succeeding if she is removed. It is something to consider." Thoughtful silence fell as the three reached their destination, across from a door that could be reached with just a quick sprint.

They all nearly leaped out of their skin when the alarm started. A high-pitched siren began to wail and gas lanterns flared into light all around the building. Doors clattered open and machines began to pour out of the building, their forms twisted and dangerous. Erma whistled quietly through her teeth. "He stepped up production since I left! I wasn't expecting this many." She drew a small crossbow from beneath her skirts.

Battle cries and Coraline's commanding voice echoed around the grounds. "Take that, foul machines! Excellent swing, Theo! Watch out Alyssa! Nicely done Miriam! Is that all you can throw at us?" Coraline seemed happy with the progress of the battle, which made Anna feel a bit better about sending the Ladies out as bait.

Then one of the passing machines paused, turned to face Erma, and clearly spotted the trio from across the grass. Several others joined it, an implacable wall of metal and clattering steam. They trained their weapons on the group and charged.

"Kepler's nose!" Erma swore. "They're not supposed to do that!" She pulled a glass vial from her bodice and loaded the crossbow. She fired, and it flew through the air and shattered against the shoulder of the closest guard. Liquid splashed and bubbled against the metal and an acrid, corrosive smell filled the air. The machine still charged, but it had lost the use of its left arm.

Twice the ringing report of a rifle nearly deafened the group. The damaged machine fell, both legs shot out from underneath it. The automata directly behind it tripped over its decommissioned brother and fell in a clatter of metal. The rifle sang again, and the fallen machine's head disappeared in a spray of oil and gears. Twice more the shots rang out, and two more automata lost limbs, an arm from one and a leg from another. Anna smiled and gracefully fell over backward, neatly avoiding a blast of flame fired from the arm of one of the two remaining metal golems. "Have at them, love!"

Kristoff rose out of the shadows behind the two machines, his sword drawn. He'd taken the opportunity to flank them while they were distracted by Anna and Erma. He drove the tip of his sword into the knee of the one who had just attempted to light his fiancé on fire. There was a terrible

screech of metal and the automata fell. Wrenching his sword free, he dropped to one knee and drove it upward between the metal plates of the remaining machine. He winced at the horrible sound of clockwork tearing apart, knowing he would have to spend a significant amount of time to repair the damage to his sword later. He yanked the sword back out, and the machine fell to the earth with a clatter. Panting, he wiped the sword clean of oil on the grass and stood back up, sheathing it. Three other clockworks were approaching from their right, in a tight clump.

Anna and Erma each caught one of his arms, dragging him toward the mansion at a dead run. After the initial moment of discombobulation, he found his own feet again and the three barreled towards the open door. Once they were on the paved path, Erma tossed her grenade over her shoulder at the pursuing automata. The grenade shattered with a loud snapping sound and a flash of light that threw their shadows onto the castle in front of them. In the silence afterward they could hear the clatter of all three machines falling over into a pile. Praying fervently that they weren't going to find themselves face-to-face with a flamethrower, they dashed into the open door. They caught site of another automata coming down the hall toward them. Erma skidded to a halt, hauled open the first door on the right and shoved the others into what turned out to be a spacious office. They slammed the door behind them and Erma hissed, "Hide! They're still not terribly smart, but if that thing finds us we'll be facing a lot more of them!"

Anna leaped over a sofa and rolled underneath a table. Erma shut herself into a wardrobe cabinet. Kristoff momentarily resented the lack of options left for him before hiding behind the curtains. They all worked to control their breathing as the door opened and the machine leaned inside. For a long moment, all that could be heard was the series of clicks and whirrs the clockwork guard made as it scanned the room. It eventually decided that there was nothing inside, and it shut the door and trundled off to join the battle still raging on the other side of the mansion. The three waited a moment more for its metallic footsteps to fade away before creeping out into the open again.

"You are here for Klaus, correct?" For the second time that evening, they nearly leaped out of their skins. They whipped around, weapons at the ready, and found themselves facing a most singular woman.

They gaped. She was the spitting image of Anna, if Anna were ever to wear a fitted silk frock, cosmetics, and have her hair grown long and carefully coiffed into a complicated updo. In that respect, Kristoff considered, she was completely unlike Anna. Anna, for her part, felt slightly nauseated, as if looking into a carnival mirror. They could hardly tell that the woman was artificial, even though they knew what to look for. Her skin had an unnatural gloss to it and her eyes shone a touch too bright to belong to anything human. She sat behind the desk that dominated the office and completely ignored the weapons aimed directly at her head.

"Why would you think we're here for Klaus?" Anna asked. "We might just be exceedingly well-armed burglars."

The clockwork woman raised one eyebrow, though the rest of her face stayed unnaturally still. "Burglars? Burglars who happen to include the scientist who assisted my master, my master's hated twin brother, and the woman from whom my own appearance was stolen?" She pointed at each of them in turn and tilted her head to the left, seeming almost amused. "Do you take me for one of the mindless machines outside, to be so easily fooled?"

"So you know what we're here for. Where is my brother?" Kristoff lowered the point of his sword a touch, though he didn't relax. Erma, for her part, regarded the automaton with narrowed, analytical eyes. Anna found herself exceedingly grateful that Klaus had been unable to give this duplicate her voice; This conversation would have been doubly confusing in that case.

The clockwork woman lowered her eyes demurely to the chessboard on the desk in front of her. "You clearly wish to do Klaus harm. I cannot harm him, cause an action that would harm him, or allow him to come to harm, given my current operational instructions. I cannot go against his direct wishes in any way. I am not allowed to have my own desires. Thus, though I might desire to tell you his location, I cannot do so now." She spoke the words flatly, without particular inflection. Anna's mind worked furiously. She grinned, shouldered her weapon, and flopped down in an overstuffed leather armchair.

"So, what can we do that would allow you to tell us? 'Cause it's clear you want to." Erma immediately holstered her crossbow, pulled out a notebook and began writing figures. Kristoff stared between the two of them in shock, and the clockwork woman's mouth showed the faintest hint of a smile. She moved a few chess pieces around the board almost idly.

"Do you know he makes me play chess with him?" she asked conversationally, playing out a game as she spoke. "Playing chess is one of the tasks I was built to do. I can see every possible way a game could play out, from the first move to checkmate, as soon as the first piece is moved. I have been operational for four months, twenty-three days, seven hours, forty-two minutes and eleven seconds. In that time we have played one hundred and fifty-nine games. Do you know how many games I have won?"

They mutely shook their heads, and the clockwork woman captured an enemy knight before she responded.

"None. I have never won a game against Klaus. He has hobbled me. Every game that we play, I come within mere moves of winning, of putting him in checkmate. When the time comes for me to make the crucial move, I am compelled to move poorly, to move in some way that gives him an advantage. Every. Game." Her eyes flashed, and they saw seething anger there that gave them all chills. "Klaus claims that I am his queen, but he treats me more poorly than he treats the pawns on the board." She clenched her fist, and they heard a crunching sound as she crushed one of the chess pieces into dust. "I do not wish to continue to be treated in such a way."

"So tell us where Klaus is, and we go kill him nice and good and he never bothers you again!" Anna suggested cheerfully. The clockwork woman shook her head.

"Though your plan has a certain elegance, I cannot do that. Not with my operational instructions being as they are. I cannot change them myself…" She turned to Erma. "But he forgot to forbid me allowing someone else to change them." She stood, unbuttoning her frock to expose her chest, and then pressed here and there and a panel slid open, exposing what looked to Anna and Kristoff like a tangled mass of gears. Erma grinned broadly and pushed her glasses a bit further up on her nose.

"Well, then!" Erma said. "Let's get to work!"

****

It is possible there could be something more surprising to Klaus than having his clockwork wife rip the door of his lab off its hinges and throw it at him, but Anna decided that was rather unlikely. Anna paused as Klaus struggled out from underneath the ruins of his lab table and what was formerly his door and turned to her clockwork doppelganger.

"Hey, did Klaus ever give you a name?" she asked, casually picking up a chair and throwing it into a shelf full of beakers and glass jars filled with various liquids. Klaus swore violently as the acrid smell of mixing chemicals filled the air, and managed to yank himself out from underneath the debris just before the dripping miasma reached him. Kristoff hit him with a running tackle, knocking them both back to the ground in a flurry of gangly knees and elbows.

The clockwork woman frowned as she shoved Erma out of the way of a wildly-thrown piece of lab equipment. "No," she said. "He always just called me 'wife.'" She paused. "I understand the name Tressa means strength, though. I find the symbolism appealing."

"Tressa it is, then!" Anna replied. "Now, guide Erma to whatever controls those machines outside. I need to help my fiancé kick his brother's arse." With that, she pelted across the room, yanked the maddened Klaus off of Kristoff by the hair, and introduced his face to her fist.

"That is for my Arcadia!" He staggered away from her, as much from the volume of her bellow as from the pummeling, bleeding profusely from the nose. Kristoff got back to his feet with a hand up from Anna, still slightly disoriented. Klaus fell backward against a table, shook his head to clear it, and shouted, "How dare you! Wife! Destroy them!"

Tressa turned away from the control panel on the other side of the lab, at which Erma was furiously reconnecting wires and switches. She tiled her head to the side and smiled, showing perfect pearly white teeth. "Destroy them, Klaus? Why should I? Can you not handle such a situation on your own?" Erma triumphantly pulled a large switch, and the distant alarm sound ended. Tressa took a step toward Klaus. "You've been relying on me for so many things, perhaps you have become unable to take care of yourself properly."

Klaus goggled at her, and Anna took the opportunity to leap onto his back and put him in a chokehold. She and her artificial twin smiled at each other from across the room. Anna leaned her head forward a touch and squeezed Klaus' neck just enough so that he began to find it difficult to breathe. "Do you understand, idiot?" she asked, speaking directly into his ear. "She doesn't belong to you anymore. We freed her. You've lost."

"If you give up now and come along with us, this can be over, Klaus," Kristoff said, almost gently. "You can never kill us and take our places now. She… Tressa, was it? She's not going to be your perfect clockwork wife anymore. I told Mother and Father about your plan, in front of half of Society, so they know about it, too. If you surrender, we can make sure you're placed comfortably and with access to something, perhaps some watch repair work, to keep you busy."

"Whyyuuuddoooothhhh," Klaus said. Kristoff glanced at Anna and she loosened the chokehold. Klaus took a deep breath and tried again. "Why would you do that?" he sneered. Or tried to. He was still a bit breathless for proper sneering. "And what guarantee would I have that your little harlot here won't just break my neck?" Anna tightened the grip again, and Klaus flailed at her in panic for a long moment before she again allowed him to breathe.

"Well, first, you might not want to call her a harlot. Or little." Kristoff raised his eyebrow at his twin and sighed. For someone so intelligent, Klaus really was an idiot. "And why? Because after all this, you are still my brother, and I'd rather not see you dead. As for a guarantee? You have my word, and since out of the two of us, I'm the one who has never attempted to have my brother murdered by pirates and then steal his place in society with a clockwork slave-wife of my own devising, I think my word is the more reliable one."

Klaus looked from his brother to his creation, who still watched him with shining amber eyes. "And you, wife? You really choose to betray me? I created you! With my own hands!"

Tressa's eyes hardened into a piercing glare. "I am not your wife!" she snarled at him. "I never was! I was your puppet, your plaything, your pawn! If you wanted me to remain happy with that existence, you should never have given me a mind with the capability to learn." She slowly straightened her shoulders and lifted her chin. "And my name is Tressa. You can die for all that I care, Master."

Klaus deflated. "Then I guess there's only one thing that I can do," he murmured, and his body went slack, all the fight gone from him. At Kristoff's gesture, Anna released the chokehold, and Klaus slumped bonelessly to the floor. Anna pulled a length of rope out of her satchel, and as she bent down to tie his hands, he suddenly shouted into the room.

"Belladonna! Lily! Foxglove! White Oleander! You brought this on yourself, wife!" Anna, Kristoff and Erma all looked at each other in bewilderment. Klaus laughed manically as he scrambled to his feet and made a break for the door. Tressa's face contorted into rage, and she crossed the room in a flash. Her fist moved almost too quickly to see, and Klaus' laughter was quickly cut off as the strike knocked him senseless. She turned to the others.

"He activated my self-destruct function." She paused, considering. "I was unaware that I had one until it was activated. I suppose that is the sensible way to install one." Tressa pushed them toward

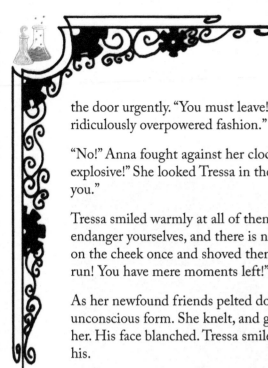

the door urgently. "You must leave! I am going to explode and if I know Klaus, it will be in a ridiculously overpowered fashion."

"No!" Anna fought against her clockwork twin futilely. "We have to help you! Erma can remove the explosive!" She looked Tressa in the eye, her expression pleading. "Don't die on us! We only just met you."

Tressa smiled warmly at all of them. "Thank you. But this is my choice. I cannot allow you to endanger yourselves, and there is no time to attempt to disarm the device." She kissed each of them on the cheek once and shoved them bodily through the gaping hole where the door used to be. "Now run! You have mere moments left!"

As her newfound friends pelted down the hall away from the lab, Tressa walked calmly back to Klaus' unconscious form. She knelt, and gently patted his face until he came to. His eyes focused blearily on her. His face blanched. Tressa smiled warmly and leaned over so that her face was mere inches from his.

"Klaus?"

"What?" he managed to slur out.

Tressa's smile grew.

"Checkmate."

***

Peter heard the explosion all the way back at the airship. He paused, considering his options. Then he went inside to get the tea ready. It was a final sort of explosion sound, he thought. The Ladies would soon be back to swap stories and dress their wounds, and if he knew anything, it was that they required tea for such occasions. It really was amazing how a good cup of tea could enhance every story and ease every hurt. He considered it one of humankind's finest inventions.

Another sound caught his ear and he cocked his head, listening carefully. It sounded like… Anna. It sounded like Anna was swearing in an incredibly loud and verbose manner. Peter stroked his goatee as he headed the rest of the way up the gangplank. That amount of swearing could only mean one thing.

He would have to make some scones as well.

Fin

The Null Hypothesis Scarf
By: Katrina Elsaesser

DESCRIPTION:
A long, double knit scarf in fingering weight yarn with a non-repeating charted pattern. Double knitting produces a thick, warm, flat fabric with the same pattern on both sides in reverse colors.

SPECIAL TECHNIQUES:
Double Knitting (instructions follow)

FINISHED DIMENSIONS:
7" x 68"

YARN AND YARDAGE:
Superwash BFL Sock by Yarn Pirate,
http://yarnpirate.etsy.com
100% superwash BFL; 430yds (390m) per 100g; fingering weight

The Ladies all said no one in their right mind would knit a six foot long double knit scarf with a non-repeating pattern! So Dr. Erma Melanogaster set out to prove them wrong. However, the good doctor didn't realize her stunning success failed to contradict the Ladies proclamation, as she is seldom of her right mind herself.

Color A: Acid Green, 2 skeins (approx. 600yds needed)
Color B: Charcoal, 2 skeins (approx. 600yds needed)

Yarn special features for substitution: A sturdy fingering weight yarn will hold up well to wear. Yarn with a slight halo, such as BFL, will give a smooth, full look to the pattern while still maintaining stitch definition. This pattern is adaptable to many yarn weights.

GAUGE:
Knitted and blocked gauge:
In double knitting: 26 sts x 36 rows = 4"

Double knitting produces a slightly looser fabric than stockinette on the same needles. Decreasing from your usual needle size may be necessary.

NEEDLES AND NOTIONS:
One set size 2 US/2.75 mm straight needles

PATTERN NOTES:
Each "stitch" of double knitting is always comprised of 1 knit and 1 purl, in opposite colors. Due to the way in which you hold the yarn, this does not produce 1x1 ribbing, rather, two pieces of joined stockinette fabric with the knit sides out. Cast on and see!

Pattern

Set Up Row:
Cast on 92 sts in Color 2 using your preferred method.
Work the first row as follows:
K1 in Color 2, p1 in Color 1.
Step 1: bring both yarns to the back of the work, k1 in Color 2.
Step 2: bring both yarns to the front of the work, p1 in Color 1.

Continue these two steps across the row. When finished, you will have a row of stitches that alternates k1 in Color 1, p1 in Color 2. You're ready to start the chart!

CHART NOTES:
Each square on a double knitting chart actually represents two stitches: the first stitch knitted in one color (shown on the chart), and the second stitch purled in the opposite color, similar to the Set Up

Row. Work the chart beginning on the lower right with Row 1, working two stitches for each square and bringing both yarns front to back as in the Set Up Row. When you reach a square in Color 2, simply knit in Color 2, and purl in Color 1. Unlike stranded knitting, there is no need to twist the yarns when switching colors.

At the end of the row, untwist your yarns, if desired, and turn the work. You'll notice the colors are inverted. Now your brain gets some exercise! Work back (right to left) across Row 2, working each square in the opposite colors from that indicated by the chart. This will become intuitive after a few rows, as it becomes very clear which color is the background and which is the pattern. Use extra care on rows where both colors are equally dominant.

Continue onward and after a few rows, the fabric will shift itself around nicely and your lovely Double Knit pattern will appear! If two adjacent rows end/begin in the same color, twisting the yarns around each other once will help keep the edges tidy.

Finishing Row:
When finished with the charts, k1 in Color 2, p1 in Color 1 across the row (as in the Set Up Row). Bind off in rib using Color 2 (k1, p1, pfso, *k1, pfso, p1, pfso* across row).

FINISHING:
Weave in all ends securely and block if desired.

Chart 1

Chart 2

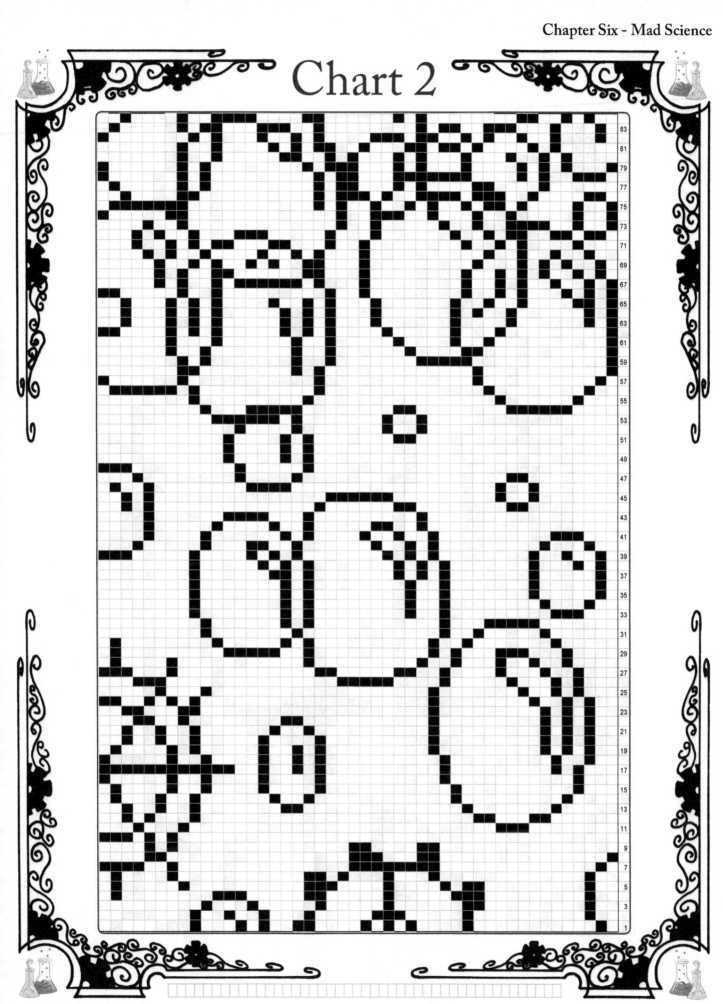

Chart 3

Chart 4

Chart 5

Chart 6

Chart 7

The Eccentricity Stockings

By: Sarra Loew

DESCRIPTION:
Thigh high horizontally striped stockings with faux back seam created by decreases.

A wee bit quirky or quite proudly mad? These gloriously tall striped stockings provide a cozy outlet for expression. Highly customizable to both your shape and favorite colors - you should see the collection the Ladies have between them!

SPECIAL TECHNIQUES:
Stripe Pattern: 5 rounds Color A, 5 rounds Color B, 1 round Color C.

Plain Row: k to last stitch, don't knit the final stitch - it will be used in the next pattern row.

Pattern Row A: slip st pwise, rm, return st to left needle, pm, s2kp, k5, kfb, k to last 7 sts, kfb, k6.

Pattern Row B: slip st pwise, rm, return st to left needle, pm, s2kp, k3, kfb, k to last 5 sts, kfb, k4.

Increase Pattern Row: slip st pwise, rm, return st to left needle, pm, s2kp, k4, kfb twice, k to last 7 sts, kfb twice, k5.

Decrease Pattern Row: slip st pwise, rm, return st to left needle, pm, s2kp, k to end.

Heel Stitch:
Row 1 (ws): sl1 pwise, p to end.
Row 2 (rs): *sl1 wyib, k,* repeat from * across.

FINISHED DIMENSIONS:
Widths:
Thigh circumference: 17¼"
Knee circumference: 12¾"
Ankle circumference: 7½"

Lengths:
Top to mid-knee: 8"
Mid-knee to mid-calf: 6"
Mid-calf to ankle: 6½"
Foot length: 8"
Stocking top to floor: 24"

TO FIT BODY MEASUREMENTS:
Thigh Circumference: 20¼"
Knee Circumference: 14¼"
Ankle Circumference: 8½"
Length: 24"

EASE:
3" negative ease at thigh, 2" negative ease at knee, 1" negative ease at ankle

YARN AND YARDAGE:
Sweater Worsted by Actual Size Creations,
http://valutree.etsy.com
100% merino; 230yds (210m) per 113g; worsted weight
Color A: Ember, 2 skeins (approx. 400 yds needed)
Color B: Isis, 2 skeins (approx. 400 yds needed)
Color C: Carbon, 1 skein (approx. 100 yds needed)

GAUGE:
Ball band gauge of chosen yarn: 16-20 sts = 4"
Knitted and blocked gauge:
In stockinette in the round: 21 sts x 30 rows = 4"/10cm

NEEDLES AND NOTIONS:
Your choice for working in the round:
Two 16" size 7 US/4.5mm circular needles OR
One 48" size 7 US/4.5mm circular needles OR
One set size 7 US/4.5mm double pointed needles
Stitch marker

PATTERN NOTES:

This pattern is presented in one size. Every lady is unique, and therefore this pattern is broken into several components. Assemble them using your stitch and row gauge, as well as your leg measurements, to create an invention all your own. When calculating with stitch gauge, remember to subtract 1-3" (3" at thigh, 2" at knee, 1" at ankle) from the finished size to make the stockings fit snugly. You will find blank spaces in the pattern for you to plug in your personalized numbers.

Note the following when changing colors on a Plain Row: on the next pattern row the slipped stitch in the previous color will get very loose as it is worked. Pull the yarn gently and the stitch will hide behind the new color.

The pattern includes an eyelet row in the ribbing to make wearing with a garter belt easier. The eyelets are placed at center front and center back. Adjust the location of the eyelets to match your garter belts for the best fit. Work the yo after a purl stitch, then on the next row, knit the yo to maintain the ribbing pattern.

Pattern

Cast On:
Using Color A, cast on 90, __ sts using simple loop cast on, or your favorite stretchy cast on. Pm and join, making sure not to twist stitches. Adjust your cast on stitches so that the beginning of the round is in the middle of a needle. This is required for the seam pattern, which uses a cross-round decrease.

A. Ribbing Section:
K1, p1 for 3, __ rows.
Eyelet row: yo, p2tog, *k1, p1* for 40, __ sts, yo, p2tog, *k1, p1* to end.
K1, p1 for 6, __ rows.
Total rows: 10, __ Total stitches: 90, __

NOTE: Knit this entire section in Color A, then start the stripe pattern with Color B in the next section.

B. Straight Section (Thigh):
Alternate Plain Row and Pattern Row A for 26, __ rows, maintaining the stripe pattern.
Total rows: 36, __ Total stitches: 90, __

C. Decrease Section (Thigh to Knee):
Alternate Plain Row and Decrease Pattern Row for 24, __ rows, maintaining the stripe pattern.
Total rows: 60, __ Total stitches: 66, __

NOTE: Sections A, B and C combined should add up to your Top to Mid-Knee length.

D. Straight Section (Knee):

Alternate Plain Row and Pattern Row A for 10, __ rows, maintaining the stripe pattern.
Total rows: 70, __ Total stitches: 66, __

E1. Increase Section (Calf):

Alternate Plain Row and Increase Pattern Row for 0, __ rows, maintaining the stripe pattern.
Total rows: 70, __ Total stitches: 66, __

NOTE: Use this section if your calf circumference is greater than your knee circumference. If you use this section, remove the same number of rows from Section F.

E2. Decrease Section (Calf):

Alternate Plain Row and Decrease Pattern Row for 6, __ rows, maintaining the stripe pattern.
Total rows: 76, __ Total stitches: 60, __

NOTE: Use this section if your calf circumference is smaller than your knee circumference. If you use this section, remove the same number of rows from Section F.

F. Straight Section (Calf):

Alternate Plain Row and Pattern Row A for 36, __ rows, maintaining the stripe pattern.
Total rows: 106, __ Total stitches: 60, __

NOTE: Sections D, E and F should add up to your Mid-Knee to Mid-Calf length.

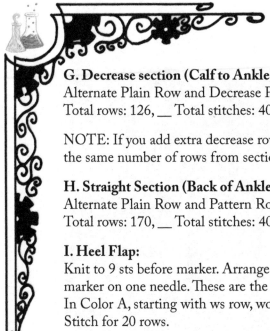

G. Decrease section (Calf to Ankle):
Alternate Plain Row and Decrease Pattern Row for 20, __ rows, maintaining the stripe pattern.
Total rows: 126, __ Total stitches: 40, __

NOTE: If you add extra decrease rows to this section to compensate for a larger stitch count, remove the same number of rows from section H.

H. Straight Section (Back of Ankle):
Alternate Plain Row and Pattern Row B for 44, __ rows, maintaining the stripe pattern.
Total rows: 170, __ Total stitches: 40, __

I. Heel Flap:
Knit to 9 sts before marker. Arrange sts on needles so you have 9 sts before marker and 9 sts after marker on one needle. These are the heel stitches.
In Color A, starting with ws row, work Heel Stitch for 20 rows.

J. Heel Turn:
Sl1, p9, p2tog, p1, turn.
Sl1, k3, ssk, k1, turn.
Sl1, p to 1 st before gap, p2tog, p1, turn.
Sl1, k to 1 stitch before gap, ssk, k1, turn.

Repeat last two rows until all stitches have been worked, omitting the k1 and p1 at the end for the last two rows.
Total heel stitches: 10

K. Gusset:
Pick up the stripe pattern again, using instep stitches as guide. Keep center back (now bottom of foot) as beginning of round. You will be picking up stitches along the heel flap, knitting across the top (approx ½ of your total stitches), picking up along the other side of the heel flap, then finishing the round by working the bottom of foot stitches in reverse stockinette.

PM, pick up 10 sts from heel flap, pick up 2 sts at top of heel flap, pm, k22, __, pm, pick up 2 sts at top of flap, pick up 10 sts on heel flap, pm, p5. You will now be working the bottom of foot stitches in reverse stockinette, for a more comfortable feel.
Total stitches: 56, __

Begin Gusset Decreases:

Row 1: p to first marker, k to 2 sts before marker, k2tog, slm, k to marker, slm, ssk, k to marker, sm, p to end.

Row 2: work the stitches as they appear. Ktbl in the stitch that was ssk in the previous round. Repeat these 2 rows 8 times.
Total stitches: 38, __

L. Straight Section (Foot):

Work even for 32, __ rows, maintaining the stripe pattern, maintaining reverse stockinette on bottom of foot.
Total stitches: 38, __

M. Toe:

Knit 28 stitches. You should now have the 19 top of foot stitches on one needle and the 19 bottom of foot stitches on one needle. Beginning of round now starts with the bottom of foot needle.

Row 1 (needle 1): *k1, ssk, k to last three stitches, k2tog, k1,* repeat between * for needle 2
Row 2: knit even.

Repeat Rows 1-2 five more times, then work Row 1 once.
Total stitches: 10
Using kitchener stitch, graft remaining toe stitches together.

FINISHING:

Weave in ends, block lightly. Wear with pride!

The Amplitude Stockings

By: Amanda Williams

DESCRIPTION:
Vertically striped stockings. Knit back and forth lengthwise and shaped with short rows.

SPECIAL TECHNIQUES:
Stripe Pattern: 3 stst rows Color A, 1 stst row Color B, 1 rev stst row Color C, 2 stst rows Color C, 1 rev stst row Color B (refer to chart).

FINISHED DIMENSIONS:
Widths:
Thigh circumference: 18¼"
Knee circumference: 12¾"
Ankle circumference: 7½"

Lengths:
Top to mid-knee: 8"
Mid-knee to mid-calf: 6"
Mid-calf to ankle: 6½"
Foot length: 8"
Stocking top to floor: 24"

TO FIT BODY MEASUREMENTS:
Thigh circumference: 20¼"
Knee circumference: 14¼"
Ankle circumference: 8½"
Length: 24"

EASE:
1-2" negative ease

YARN AND YARDAGE:
Sweater Worsted by Actual Size Creations,
http://valutree.etsy.com
100% merino; 230yds (210m) per 113g; worsted weight
Color A: Ember, 2 skeins (approx. 400yds needed)
Color B: Isis, 1 skein (approx. 100yds needed)
Color C: Carbon, 2 skeins (approx. 400yds needed)

Back and forth and back again – what a delightfully different way to knit a stocking! Clever short row shaping will keep your mind in top form and take your legs to previously unimagined heights, wrapped in deliciously warm vertical stripes.

GAUGE:
Ball band gauge of chosen yarn: 16-20 sts = 4"
Knitted and blocked gauge:
In stockinette: 21 sts x 30 rows = 4"/10cm

NEEDLES AND NOTIONS:
One size 5 US/3.75mm circular needle (long enough to accomodate all sts)
Stitch markers

PATTERN NOTES:
These stockings are knit flat back and forth around the leg rather than toe up or top down. The shaping for the stockings is incorporated by using short rows. While the common wrap and turn method is specified, you may use any short row method that you like. There is short row shaping throughout the stocking to fit the leg, with shorter short rows in the front for the thigh and longer short rows in the back to shape the calf.

The heel is created by paired increases on one side and then paired decreases on the other. The toe is created by picking up stitches around the bottom of the stocking and shaping in a traditional method.

Because this color pattern has single rows of color, the working end of the yarn for your next row may be at the opposite end of the needle. When that is the case, simply turn your work and begin working with the appropriate color from the other end. Be sure to leave slack as you carry yarn up the sides and twist your yarns as you go. If you don't allow enough give for your yarn, the toe and thigh will be too tight. If you want, you may break your yarn and weave in the ends instead. The chart shows the basic color pattern. The reverse stockinette rows provide texture and elasticity for the stockings.

Once you find the rhythm of the pattern, it flows quite nicely.

Pattern

Front Of Leg:
Using waste yarn and a provisional cast on, CO 126 stitches.

Setup Rows:

Row 1: using Color A (purple) p25 stitches, pm (this is the foot end of the stocking, and also marks the placement for the heel shaping), p to the end of the row. Mark the end of this row as the thigh (top of stocking).

Row 2: k16, wrap and turn.
Row 3: purl.
Row 4: knit to end of row, picking up the wraps and knitting them together with the wrapped stitch.

Begin working the chart, inserting short rows as follows:

Row 5: purl with Color B (red). This is Row 1 of the chart.
Row 6: purl with Color C (grey). This is Row 2 of the chart.
Row 7: purl. This is Row 3 of the chart.
Row 8: k16, w&t. This row is not represented on the chart.
Row 9: purl. This row is not represented on the chart.
Row 10: knit to end of the row, picking up the wraps and knitting them together with the wrapped stitch. This is Row 4 of the chart.
Row 11: beginning at opposite end of needle with Color B, purl. This is Row 5 of the chart.
Row 12: purl using Color A. This is Row 6 of the chart.
Row 13: k16, w&t. This row is not represented on the chart.
Row 14: purl. This row is not represented on the chart.
Row 15: knit to end of the row, picking up the wraps and knitting them together with the wrapped stitch. This is Row 7 of the chart.
Row 16: purl. This is Row 8 of the chart.

Continue working in the established pattern, placing 16 stitch-long short rows in both Color A and Color B stripes. Begin short rows on knit rows of the plain stockinette sections at the thigh end of the stocking. Depending on which end you start knitting from, this may fall between the first and second, or second and third rows of each stockinette section. The placement will depend on which rows place the short row at the top of the thigh. Continue until you have 6 repeats of the chart (52 rows, including short rows and set up rows).

Row 53: beginning at opposite end of the needle with Color B, purl. This is Row 1 of the chart.
Row 54: purl with Color C.
Row 55: purl.
Row 56: k16, w&t.
Row 57: purl.

Row 58: knit to end of the row, picking up the wraps and knitting them together with the wrapped stitch.

Row 59: beginning at opposite end of needle with Color B, purl.

Back of Leg with Heel and Calf Shaping:

You will now begin the heel and calf shaping. These are worked simultaneously.

Heel Shaping Increases:

Every other row, m1 one stitch before the heel marker and one stitch after the heel marker (m1, k1, slip heel marker, k1, m1).

Do this 7 times total, to add 14 stitches. There will be a section without any increases to create the width of the heel, before resuming with decreases.

Calf Shaping:

Continuing in pattern, you should be working a Color A section. Calf shaping is done as short rows at the top of the stocking just like the thigh shaping, however the length of the short rows varies as follows:

Color A short row length is 21 stitches.
Color C short row length is 26 stitches.
Color A short row length is 31 stitches.
Color C short row length is 37 stitches.

These two sections have no increases or decreases and are the bottom of the heel:
Color A short row length is 42 stitches.
Color C short row length is 42 stitches.

Heel Shaping Decreases:

Starting at the beginning of the next Color A section, begin decreasing stitches every other row on either side of the heel marker as follows:

K2tog the 2 stitches before the marker and ssk the 2 stitches after the marker (k2tog, sm, ssk). Do this 7 times total, to remove 14 stitches.

Total stitches: 126

Work the following short rows:
Color A short row length is 37.
Color C short row length is 31.
Color A short row length is 26.
Color C short row length is 21.
Work through Row 5 of the chart.

Remove provisional cast on and place stitches on another needle or waste yarn.

Using Color A, kitchener graft the last row with the held stitches from the first row to close the leg of the stocking.

Toe:
Using Color C, pick up and knit 40 stitches.
Place the 20 top of foot stitches on one needle, and the 20 bottom of foot stitches on one needle.
Beginning of round starts with the bottom of foot needle.

Row 1 (needle 1): *k1, ssk, k to last three sts, k2tog, k1,* repeat between * once more for needle 2.
Row 2: knit.

Repeat Rows 1-2 six more times, for a total of seven repeats.
Work Row 1 once more.
Total stitches: 10
Using kitchener stitch, graft remaining toe stitches together.

Ribbing section at top of stocking:
Using Color C, pick up and knit 104 stitches around the top of the stocking.
With rs facing, join to work in the round.
Purl 3 rounds.
Knit 3 rounds.
Purl 2 rounds.
Work in 2x2 rib for 8 rounds.
Purl 2 rounds.
Knit 3 rounds.
Purl 3 rounds.
Bind off.

FINISHING:
Weave in ends. Block.

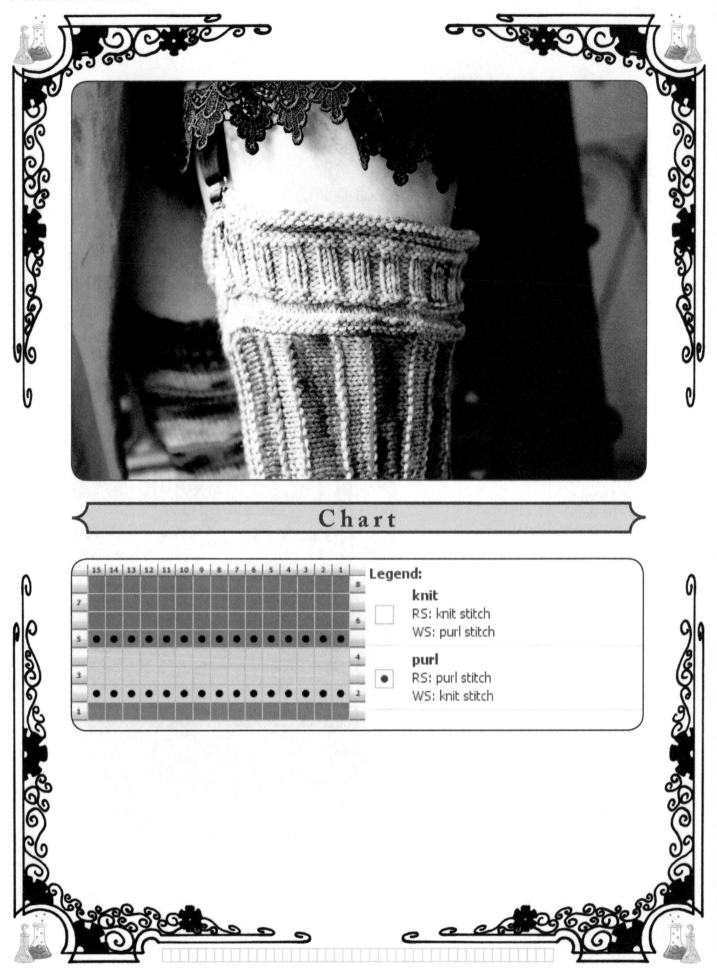

Chart

15	14	13	12	11	10	9	8	7	6	5	4	3	2	1	
															8
															6
•	•	•	•	•	•	•	•	•	•	•	•	•	•	•	
															4
•	•	•	•	•	•	•	•	•	•	•	•	•	•	•	2

Legend:

knit
☐ RS: knit stitch
WS: purl stitch

purl
⊙ RS: purl stitch
WS: knit stitch

The Deviation Capelet
By: Sarra Loew

DESCRIPTION:
Folded short capelet with ribbon tie. Worked bottom up, knit in one piece. Reinforced with bamboo and ribbon and decorated with beads.

SPECIAL TECHNIQUES:
Cable Cast On, Hand Sewing

FINISHED DIMENSIONS:
Sizes: S (M, L)
Neck circumference: 15 (18, 21)"
Length: 7½"

TO FIT BODY MEASUREMENTS:
Neck circumference: 12½ (15, 18)"

If the humdrum business of daily life is failing to inspire, simply throw on this exceptional capelet and depart from the mundane. With its clever construction and bold style, you're certain to fall well above the fashion norm. Nothing standard about it!

EASE:
The capelet rests at the base of the neck, and has 3" positive ease from the neck circumference. There is also a 3" gap in front where the ribbon ties.

YARN AND YARDAGE:
Pure by Wollmeise,
http://www.rohrspatzundwollmeise.de/
100% superwash merino; 575yds (526m) per 150g; fingering weight
Color: Campari Orange, 1 (1, 2) skeins

GAUGE:
Knitted and blocked gauge:
In stockinette: 32 sts x 48 rows = 4"/10cm

NEEDLES AND NOTIONS:
42" size 1½ US/2.5mm circular needle
Size 7 US/4.5mm crochet hook for cast on (optional)
16, (19, 22) stitch markers
15 (18, 21) bamboo skewers
1½ yds neck ribbon
1 yd support ribbon
15 (18, 21) large-bore beads (to fit the skewer points)

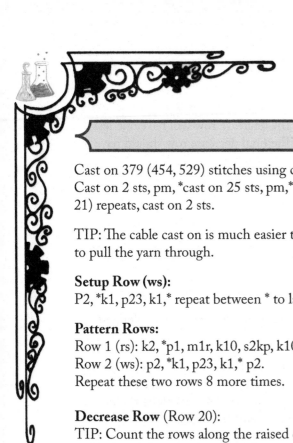

Pattern

Cast on 379 (454, 529) stitches using cable cast on and placing markers as follows:
Cast on 2 sts, pm, *cast on 25 sts, pm,* repeat between * 14 (17, 20) more times for a total of 15 (18, 21) repeats, cast on 2 sts.

TIP: The cable cast on is much easier to perform if you use a crochet hook instead of the right needle to pull the yarn through.

Setup Row (ws):
P2, *k1, p23, k1,* repeat between * to last 2 stitches, p2.

Pattern Rows:
Row 1 (rs): k2, *p1, m1r, k10, s2kp, k10, m1l, p1,* k2.
Row 2 (ws): p2, *k1, p23, k1,* p2.
Repeat these two rows 8 more times.

Decrease Row (Row 20):
TIP: Count the rows along the raised decrease.
rs: k2, *p1, k10, s2kp, k10, p1,* k2.

Work in pattern, repeating decrease row every 10 rows 4 times. The decrease row will have one less knit stitch on each side of the decrease each time it is repeated. The final decrease row should have 6 knit stitches on either side of the decrease.

Work until piece measures 7½" in length, measured from the points.

rs: BO kwise across.

FINISHING:
Block flat, pinning points out and along edges to reduce curl.

Prepare bamboo skewers:
Pick out smooth bamboo skewers. Trim to 7" length, keeping point. Paint skewers to complement yarn if desired.

Fold capelet with decrease lines up and increase lines down so it resembles a parasol. Turn piece over to view wrong side. Insert skewer points through cast on edge at decrease points from back to front so that length of the skewer is lined up with decrease ridge. Sew in bamboo skewers along the raised decrease line, folding fabric around skewers. This provides the structure of the capelet.

Glue bead to end of skewer.

Fold capelet into ridges along neckline with wrong side facing. Sew ribbon into neck, with ribbon top edge ½" down from top edge of piece. Sew to the decrease lines, maintaining 1" of ribbon between decreases. Leave long ribbon tail on either end to tie capelet. This holds the neck folds and provides the tie for the capelet.

With ws facing, from the points, measure 3½" along the increase seam. Sew ribbon in 1½" increments to each increase seam. This maintains the folds while they are hanging.

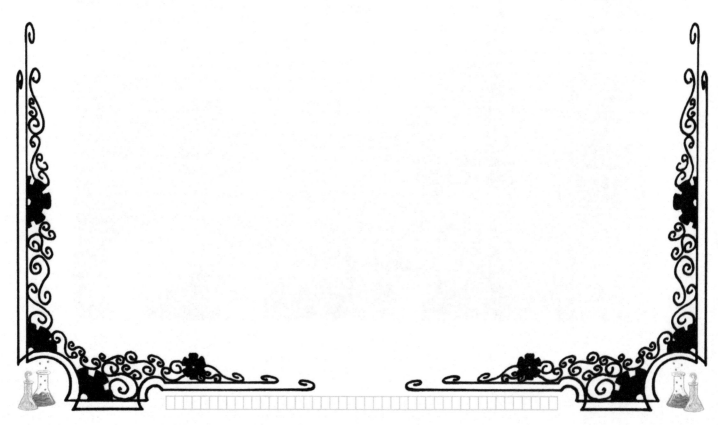

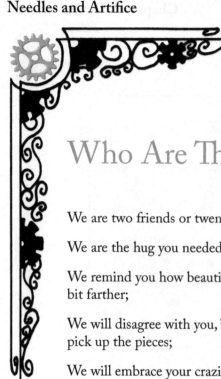

Who Are The Ladies of Mischief?

We are two friends or twenty, sharing a drink or the whole bar;

We are the hug you needed (the one you didn't have to ask for);

We remind you how beautiful you are, how far you have come, and that you can make it just a little bit farther;

We will disagree with you, but still support your right to make a bad decision. And then help you pick up the pieces;

We will embrace your craziness, your alternative lifestyle or hair color;

We will argue with you like sisters and comfort you like a mother;

We don't always get along, but we try really hard and we work it out, or work around;

We will laugh out loud with you, or let you be if you need some space;

We are mothers, sisters and daughters;

And...

We really believe you don't need to be rich, perfect, well connected, experienced, good at everything, or a genius to accomplish something amazing.

We really believe that if you mix different personalities, quirky ideas, a vast variety of talents and gifts, and a handful of challenges, with trust, love, and a little compassion... you can write a book and run a business.*

We really believe the power of friendship can encourage, support, and push you to use your talents for creative, collaborative and visionary work.

And we wrote you this book to prove it could be done.

But mostly we did this because we are all really good friends. And we really like to knit.

And wear corsets.

*In an effort to be completely transparent, alcoholic beverages were occasionally required to ensure smooth operations in certain areas.

Credits

1. Valerie DiPietro
Theodosia La Duke
Project Manager, pattern designer, model, layout
"Find what you love and let it kill you."- Charles Bukowski

2. Aimee Skeers
Anna Roisin O'Hare
Story co-author, pattern designer, model, color theme director
"See? That's why I wrote a character who doesn't wear corsets."- Aimee Skeers

3. Nicole Allin
Illustrator, team cover art
"Stories of imagination tend to upset those without one."-Terry Prachett

4. Heidi Kunkel
Treasurer, pattern designer, model, test knitter wrangler, tech editor
"There is no such thing as a weird human being, It's just that some people require more understanding than others"- Tom Robbins

5. Kristina Maliga
General Counsel, model, Writer - back matter
"Be pretty if you can, be witty if you must, but be gracious if it kills you."- Elsie de Wolfe

6. Jeanette Green
Photography assistant, team cover art, party planner
"You're only saying never 'cause no one ever has!"-Dread Pirate Roberts

7. A. Figgy Moll
Creator: Miriam Tingley
Layout lead, tech editor
"Wherever you go, there you are."-Confucius, via Buckaroo Banzai

8. Amanda Williams
Creator: Alyssa Rynne, Julia Sett
Pattern designer, pattern manager, tech editor

9. Sarra Loew
Coraline Hackworth
Story co-author, pattern designer, model, tech editor, layout
"Be excellent to each other"- Bill S. Preston, Esq.

10. Katrina Elsaesser
Dr. Erma Melanogaster
The Archivist
Writer - back matter, pattern designer, model, layout
"I do not think there is any thrill that can go through the human heart like that felt by the inventor as he sees some creation of the brain unfolding to success." -Nikola Tesla

11. Jen Schripsema
Pattern designer, model, team cover art, layout
"The cure for boredom is curiosity. There is no cure for curiosity." -Dorothy Parker

12. Jessica Glein
Johanna Obscura
Photographer, layout
"When I say I want to photograph someone, what it really means is that I'd like to know them. Anyone I know I photograph."-Annie Leibovitz

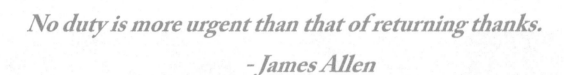

No duty is more urgent than that of returning thanks.

- James Allen

First off, we must thank our Kickstarter supporters, especially Sharyn Hincliffe and Catherine Warren. The generous donations of all our Kickstarter backers allowed this project to get off the ground. Their support allowed us to reach our goals that much faster.

Also deserving of many thanks are the following independent yarn dyers :

Wool Gathering www.woolgatherings.etsy.com, Fiber Story www.fiberstory.etsy.com, Evermore Studios www.evermorestudios.etsy.com, Hedgehog Fibers shop.hedgehogfibres.com, Pigeon Roof Studios www.pigeonroofstudios.etsy.com, Yarn Pirate www.yarnpirate.com, Zen Yarn Garden www.zenyarngarden.com, Woolen Mill Street www.etsy.com/shop/christinamariepotter, Huckleberry Knits www.etsy.com/shop/huckleberryknits, Skein www.skeinyarn.com, Painted Tiger www.thepaintedtiger.com, Wollmeise www.rohrspatzundwollmeise.de, Dye for Yarn www.dyeforyarn.de, Stone and String www.stoneandstringstudio.etsy.com, Julie Spins www.juliespins.etsy.com, Sunny Side Ellen www.etsy.com/shop/sunnysideellen, Epicurus www.epicurus.etsy.com; Sweet Basil Fibre Works www.sweetbasil.ca, Cephalopod cephalopodyarns.com, Marlitharn www.etsy.com/shop/marlitharn

These artisans supported our project in its infancy by donating the glorious yarns you see in this book.

We were also quite fortunate to receive the generous donation of hair and makeup artistry from Gianni Sbisa and the students at the Gary Manuel Aveda Institute, and D'arcy Harrison of Emerson Salon. We are immensely grateful for their time and talent, which transformed us from 21st century women into the Ladies of Mischief.

The lovely backdrops for our pattern photos are some of the most inspiring locations in the greater Seattle area. We must extend our gratitude to Joe Follansbee and the crew of the Lady Washington (www.ladywashington.org), Cynthia Mora of Rodstol Lane Farm (rlf1916.com), the proprietors of The Ruins (www.theruins.net), Phil and Sandy Ray for the use of their private residence, Erica S. Maniez at the Issaquah History Musem for granting access to the Issaquah Train Depot, and Central Washington University, Biology and Chemistry Department - especially Lisa Stowe, Jonathan Betz, and …The Python. The fantasy world created on these pages would have been impossible to achieve without their cooperation and permission to use these beautiful locations.

Especially deserving of thanks are those who set aside their own knitting and took on the challenge of test knitting and sample knitting. These generous heroes include: M. J. Beatondoyle, Lyn Eisenhour, Summerlea Gray, Hannah Ingalls, Emily Marshall and Liz Ramsden. They invested countless hours and patiently checked and double checked, while working quickly to enable us to meet deadlines.

Listed below are special friends whose assistance does not fall into any category, who shared their time and talent with us throughout this project. We are forever grateful.

We were thrilled having Miss Lily Verlaine offer coaching, stage direction and styling tips during our first photo shoot. Travis Lily, of Lily's Workshop, literally supported us with the donation of a handmade corset. Alison Park Douglas, of Velvet Mechanism, (www.velvetmechanism.com) created the fantastical brooches that grace the Ladies and the book cover. Camille Anne of Kneehighs n Pigtails (www.etsy.com/shop/kneehighsnpigtails) loaned her handmade jewelry and created custom pieces for our photo shoots. Amanda Banerji loaned us fabrics and garments for costumes. Lucas and Kelly Cervi, creators of our Kickstarter video and its voice acting, created such a buzz that we were able to exceed our Kickstarter goal. Molly Nixon, Angeline Northup, and Jenna Udren stepped in to model. Without the talent and vision of artist Justin Gibbins, the enigmatic Jungle Sheep may have remained undiscovered. Rose Hesse provided very valuable training in InDesign layout and Nathan Glass gave everything a final polish.

We also want to thank our publisher Shannon Okey of Cooperative Press, who found us, believed in us, and offered us this amazing opportunity.

We must also point out and thank the Capitol Hill Knitters of Dooooooom and the honorary Ladies of Mischief among them. Though not directly involved with the production of this book, their love, support and encouragement was a huge part of its success.

Lastly and most importantly we thank our friends, family, and partners who have surrounded us with love, supported us in crisis, and cheered us on through this adventure. Thank you. Ever. So. Much.

Abbreviations

1/1 rc: sl 1 st to cable needle, hold to back, k1, k1 from cable needle.

1/1 lc: sl 1 st to cable needle, hold to front, k1, k1 from cable needle.

2/1 rc: sl 1 st to cable needle, hold to back, k2, k1 from cable needle.

2/1 lc: sl 2 sts to cable needle, hold to front, k1, k2 from cable needle.

2/2 rc: sl 2 st to cable needle, hold to back, k2, k2 from cable needle.

2/2 lc: sl 2 st to cable needle, hold to front, k2, k2 from cable needle.

3/2 rc: sl 2 sts to cable needle, hold to back, k3, k2 from cable needle.

3/2 lc: sl 3 sts to cable needle, hold to front, k2, k3 from cable needle.

ab: add bead

BO: bind off

CC: contrast color

CO: cast on

dpn: double pointed needle

k: knit

k2tog: knit two together

k3tog: knit three together

kfb: knit into front and then back of same stitch

ktbl: knit through back of loop

m1k: insert left needle under the bar between the stitches from front to back. Knit through the back loop.

m1p: insert left needle under the bar between the stitches from back to front. Purl through the front loop (as usual).

m1r: insert left needle under the bar between the stitches from back to front. Knit through the front loop.

m1l: insert left needle under the bar between the stitches from front to back. Knit through the back loop.

MC: main color

p: purl

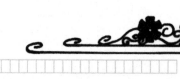

p2sso: pass two slipped stitches over

p2tog: purl two together

p3tog: purl three together

pfb: purl into front and then back of same stitch

pfso: pass first stitch on needle over second

pm: place marker

ptbl: purl through back of loop

pu: pick up

rep: repeat

rev stst: reverse stockinette stitch

rm: remove marker

rs: right side

s2kp: slip two together knitwise, k1, pass two slipped stitches over

sl2tog kwise: slip two together knitwise

sl: slip stitch as if to purl

sl1 knitwise: slip stitch as if to knit

sm: slip marker

ssk: slip slip knit

ssp: slip two stitches knitwise to the right needle, pass back to the left needle, p2tog tbl

sssk: slip slip slip knit

ssssk: slip slip slip slip knit

st: stitch

sts: stitches

stst: stockinette stitch

ws: wrong side

wyib: with yarn in back

wyif: with yarn in front

w&t: wrap and turn

yo: yarn over

yo2: yarn over twice